Introduction

This is the second of two textbooks covering Foundation Tier GCSE. Students following a two year course would expect to take one year on each book, those on a one year course half that time. The books cover the requirements of Foundation Tier GCSE and so are suitable for use with any syllabus. The division of material between them is made on the basis of the modules within the MEI syllabus. They also cover the mathematics requirements of GNVQ Application of Number at Levels 1 and 2.

This book is divided into 17 chapters, forming a logical progression through the material (some teachers may however wish to vary this order). Each chapter is divided into a number of double-page spreads, designed to be teaching units. The material to be taught is covered on the left-hand page; the right-hand pages consist entirely of work for the students to do. Each chapter ends with a mixed exercise covering all of its content. Further work sheets and tests are provided in the Teacher's Resource.

The instruction (i.e. left-hand) pages have been designed to help teachers engage their students in whole class discussion. The symbol is used to indicate a discussion point; teachers should see it as an invitation.

Each of the right-hand pages ends with a practical activity. These are suitable for both GCSE and GNVQ students; some can be used for portfolio tasks. Advice on these is available in the Teacher's Resource and, where relevant, data is also supplied. Most students will not do all of the activities (they are quite time-consuming) but the authors think it is important that they do some of them in order to connect the mathematics classroom to the outside world and to other subjects.

Where knowledge is assumed, this is stated at the start of the chapter, but in addition, there is a general expectation that students will know the four rules of basic arithmetic and be able to carry out simple long multiplication and division. Questions are expected to be answered without the use of a calculator (except for checking), unless the calculator icon indicates otherwise.

Although students are to be encouraged to use I.T., particularly spreadsheets, specific guidance is limited to the Teacher's Resource. Otherwise, the book would have been based on one particular package to the frustration of those using all the others.

The authors would like to thank those who helped in preparing this book, particularly Geoff Dunn and Julian Thomas for their advice on early versions of the manuscript, and Karen Eccles who has typed many a page.

Contents

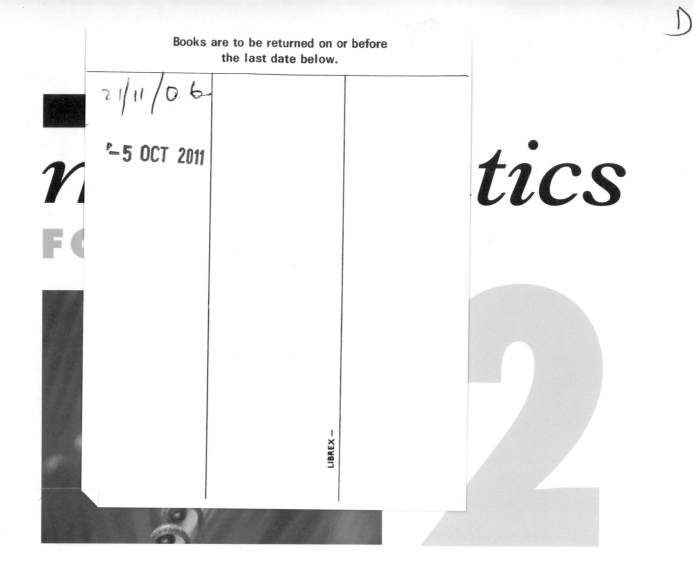

tics

F

2

Series editor: **Roger Porkess**

Catherine Berry
Dave Faulkner
Geoff Rigby
John Spencer

Maths Workshop

Hodder & Stoughton

A MEMBER OF THE HODDER HEADLINE GROUP

Acknowledgements

The authors and publishers would like to thank the following companies, agencies and individuals who have given permission to reproduce copyright material: Chris Brady, Ernest Danzig of Diplex Limited, Andrew Eeles of Her Majesty's Stationery Office, GMPTE, McDonald's, NatWest, The Royal Bank of Scotland. Every effort has been made to trace and acknowledge ownership of copyright. The publishers will be glad to make suitable arrangements with any copyright holder whom it has not been possible to contact.

Illustrations were drawn by Maggie Brand, Tom Cross, Bill Donohoe, Ann Kronheimer and Joseph McEwan.

Photos supplied by Cordon Art B.V. (page 48). The photo on page 169 appears by courtesy of the Driving Standards Agency.

Page design and cover design by Lynda King.

Orders: please contact Bookpoint Ltd, 39 Milton Park, Abingdon, Oxon OX14 4TD.
Telephone: (44) 01235 400414, Fax: (44) 01235 400454. Lines are open from 9.00 – 6.00,
Monday to Saturday, with a 24 hour message answering service. Email address: orders@bookpoint.co.uk

British Library Cataloguing in Publication Data

A catalogue record for this title is available from The British Library

ISBN 0 340 705 493

First published 1998
Impression number   10 9 8 7 6 5 4 3 2 1
Year   2004 2003 2002 2001 2000 1999 1998

Copyright © 1998 Catherine Berry, Dave Faulkner, Geoff Rigby, John Spencer

Cover photo from Photonica

Typeset by Multiplex Techniques Ltd, Orpington, Kent.

Printed in Great Britain for Hodder & Stoughton Education, a division of Hodder Headline Plc, 338 Euston Road, London NW1 3BH by Scotprint Ltd, Musselburgh, Scotland.

Contents

Information

How to use this book

This symbol next to a question means you are allowed to use your calculator. Don't use your calculator if you can't see the symbol!

This symbol means you will need to think carefully about a point. Your teacher may ask you to join in a discussion about it.

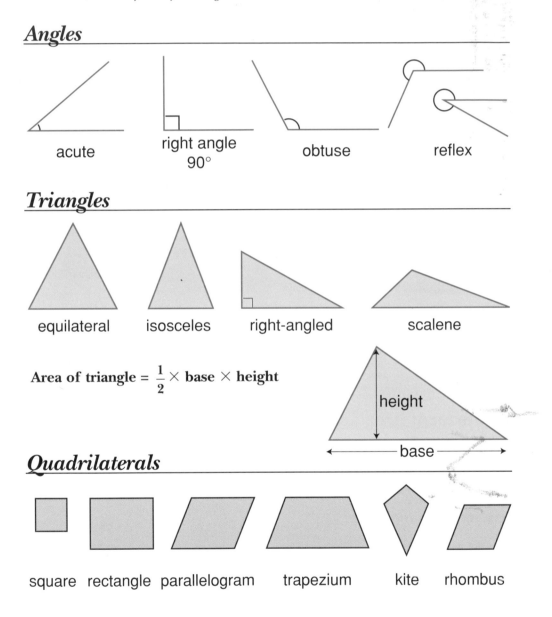

Angles

acute

right angle
90°

obtuse

reflex

Triangles

equilateral

isosceles

right-angled

scalene

Area of triangle $= \frac{1}{2} \times$ **base** $\times$ **height**

height

base

Quadrilaterals

square   rectangle   parallelogram   trapezium   kite   rhombus

Circles

Circumference of circle $= \pi \times$ diameter
$\qquad\qquad\qquad\quad = 2 \times \pi \times$ radius

Area of circle $= \pi \times (\text{radius})^2$

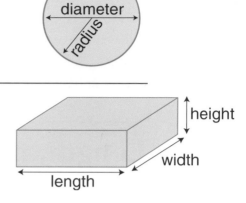

Solid figures

Volume of cuboid = length $\times$ width $\times$ height

Units

Metric system

Length	**Mass**	**Capacity**
1000 metres = 1 kilometre	1000 grams = 1 kilogram	1000 litres = 1 kilolitre
1000 millimetres = 1 metre	1000 milligrams = 1 gram	1000 millilitres = 1 litre

100 centimetres = 1 metre
10 millimetres = 1 centimetre

kilo = 1000 times

centi $= \dfrac{1}{100}$ times

milli $= \dfrac{1}{1000}$ times

Approximate conversions

1 km $= \dfrac{5}{8}$ miles $\qquad\qquad$ 1 foot = 30.5 cm

1 m = 39.37 inches $\qquad\qquad$ 1 inch = 25.4 mm

1 kg = 2.2 pounds (lb) $\qquad\qquad$ 1 pound = 454 g

1 litre $= 1\dfrac{3}{4}$ pints $\qquad\qquad$ 1 gallon = 4.5 litres

Long multiplication and long division examples

434×14

$$
\begin{array}{r}
434 \\
14 \\
\hline
4340 \\
1736 \\
\hline
6076 \\
\end{array}
$$

Answer: 6067

$434 \div 14$

$$
\begin{array}{r}
31 \\
14\overline{)434} \\
42 \\
\hline
14 \\
14 \\
\hline
\cdot\cdot \\
\end{array}
$$

Answer: 31

One

Using numbers

Length, mass and capacity

You may need to use both Imperial and metric units.

12 inches = 1 foot	**10 mm = 1 cm**
3 feet = 1 yard	**100 cm = 1 m**
1760 yards = 1 mile	**1000 m = 1 km**

When you just need a rough answer, you can use:

1 inch is about 2.5 cm

5 miles is about 8 km

 How far away is Swansea in km?

16 ounces = 1 pound	**1000 g = 1 kg**
14 pounds = 1 stone	**1000 kg = 1 tonne**
160 stones = 1 ton	

When you just need a rough answer, you can use:

1 ounce is about 28 g

1 kg is about 2.2 pounds

 How heavy is this suitcase in pounds?

8 pints = 1 gallon	**1000 ml = 1 litre**

When you just need a rough answer, you can use:

1 pint is about 0.6 litre

1 litre is about $1\frac{3}{4}$ pints

1 gallon is about $4\frac{1}{2}$ litres

 How many litres in half a pint of lemonade?

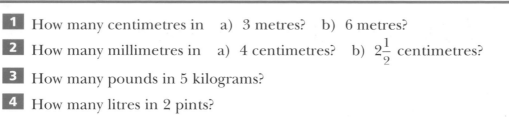

Using numbers

1 How many centimetres in   a) 3 metres?   b) 6 metres?

2 How many millimetres in   a) 4 centimetres?   b) $2\frac{1}{2}$ centimetres?

3 How many pounds in 5 kilograms?

4 How many litres in 2 pints?

5 a) How far is Sheffield from Nottingham?

   b) How far is the shortest journey shown from Lincoln to Stoke?

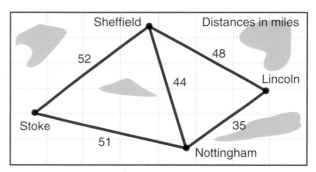

6 Pierre drives out of Dover and sees this sign (in miles). How far in kilometres is

   a) Canterbury?

   b) London?

| London | 70 |
| Canterbury | 15 |

7 Write down these readings. (They are in kilograms.)

   a)

   b)

8 A bottle contains 2 litres of lemonade.

   a) How many millilitres in this?

   b) How many 250 millilitre cans is this equal to?

9 Paul buys three 330 ml cans and Emily buys a litre bottle.

   a) Who gets more and by how much?

   b) Give two possible reasons why Paul bought the cans rather than a bottle.

Measure at least 8 everyday objects to find things

a) about 1 foot long

b) about 1 metre long

Now weigh at least 8 everyday objects to find things

c) which weigh about 1 kilogram

d) which weigh about 5 pounds.

Time

There are 24 hours in a day.

How many minutes in 1 hour?

How many seconds in 1 minute?

You can tell the time by splitting the day into 2 lots of 12 hours and using a.m. and p.m.

before midday

after midday

Another way to tell the time is to use the 24 hour clock.

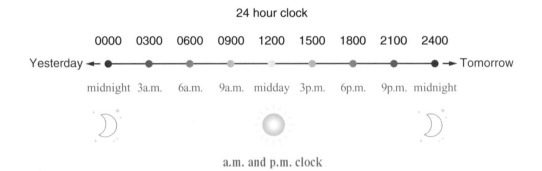

24 hour clock

| 0000 | 0300 | 0600 | 0900 | 1200 | 1500 | 1800 | 2100 | 2400 |

Yesterday ← ● — ● — ● — ● — ● — ● — ● — ● → Tomorrow

midnight 3a.m. 6a.m. 9a.m. midday 3p.m. 6p.m. 9p.m. midnight

a.m. and p.m. clock

Timetables normally use the 24 hour clock.

What is 3.15 p.m. in the 24 hour clock?

What is 1700 in a.m. or p.m.?

Example

A train leaves Aberdeen at 11 a.m. and arrives in Dundee $2\frac{1}{2}$ hours later. What time does it arrive in Dundee?

Solution

Using the 24 hour clock you say

$$1100 + 230 = 1330$$

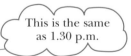

This is the same as 1.30 p.m.

This looks easy but you must be careful.
The last two digits are minutes and there are only 60 minutes in 1 hour.

A train leaves at 1140 hours and takes 1 hour 30 minutes.

What time does it arrive?

1 Using the 24 hour clock, what time is

a) half past eight in the morning?

b) 6.30 p.m.?

c) 11.20 a.m.?

2 Using a.m. or p.m., what time is

a) 0945?

b) 2230?

c) 1215?

3 A train leaves Birmingham at 1357.

It takes $1\frac{1}{2}$ hours to get to London.

a) What time does it get to London?

b) The next day, the train is 5 minutes late leaving Birmingham.

What time does it leave Birmingham?

4 In a 4 × 400 metre relay, these are the times taken to run each leg.

a) Who runs the fastest?

b) Who runs the slowest?

c) What is the total time in minutes and seconds?

Roger   52 seconds
Mike   52 seconds
Darren   53 seconds
Derek   51 seconds

5 a) How long is

(i) The News?

(ii) Local News?

(iii) Westenders?

b) Spanish Holiday is 65 minutes long.

What time does it end?

17.40	The News
18.00	Local News
18.35	Westenders
19.05	Spanish Holiday
	Forester

Time at least 12 television adverts.

How long do the longest and shortest last?

What is a typical length?

Directed numbers

Shola has £50 in her bank account. She has these bills to pay:

 How much is left in her account if she pays the telephone?

How much is left if she pays the electricity?

How much is left if she pays the car repairs?

The bank might not pay a £60 cheque when Shola has only £50 left in her account.

Or they might pay the cheque and let Shola be overdrawn by £10. In this case, her balance is −£10.

You can see this on the **number line**.

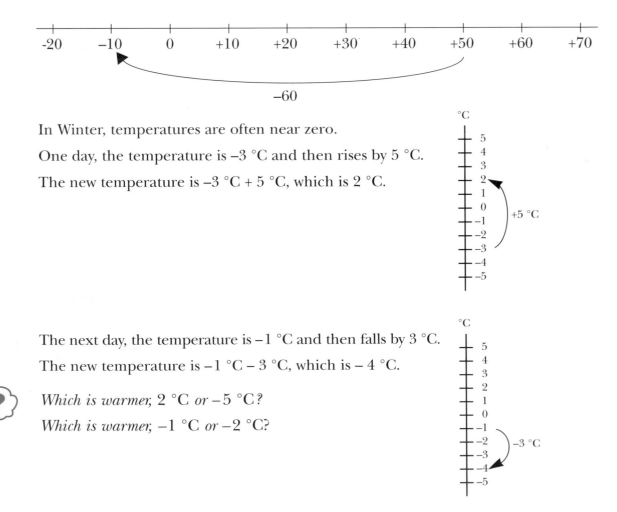

In Winter, temperatures are often near zero.

One day, the temperature is −3 °C and then rises by 5 °C.

The new temperature is −3 °C + 5 °C, which is 2 °C.

The next day, the temperature is −1 °C and then falls by 3 °C.

The new temperature is −1 °C − 3 °C, which is − 4 °C.

Which is warmer, 2 °C or − 5 °C?

Which is warmer, −1 °C or −2 °C?

1 Look at the number line on the opposite page. Shola starts with £50.

How much does she have left if she pays

a) £10?   b) £5?   c) £70?

2 The temperature is 1 °C. It falls by 3 °C.

What is the new temperature?

3 This chart shows Hana's temperature when she was in hospital.

From Monday to Tuesday, Hana's temperature falls from 38.5 to 37.9 °C.

This is a 0.6 °C fall. ◀ $38.5 - 37.9 = 0.6$

What rise or fall is there

a) from Tuesday to Wednesday?

b) from Wednesday to Thursday?

c) from Thursday to Friday?

Day	Temperature (°C)
Mon	38·5
Tue	37·9
Wed	37·3
Thu	36·9
Fri	37·0

4 Victoria has £140 in her bank account on 8 June.

She keeps this record of her money:

Victoria's bank lets her be overdrawn. Work out her balance after each of the transactions.

June 9   Paid gas bill £80
June 11 Got cheque for travel expenses £33
June 13 Paid rent £72
June 17 Paid dentist £128
June 19 Got cheque from mum £15
June 30 Got salary £550

5 A and B are two shops.

Find the total profit or loss when

a) A makes a profit of £28 000 and B makes a loss of £15 000.

b) A makes a profit of £6000 and B makes a loss of £11 000.

c) A makes a loss of £2000 and B makes a loss of £9000.

6 Work out

a) $4 - 7$ b) $-3 + 5$

c) $9 - 6$ d) $-4 - 4$

e) $8 - 3 + 4$ f) $-2 + 7 - 5$

This diagram shows the leader board in a golf competition.

	HOLE	SCORE
FALDO	11	-8
WOODS	18	-6
WOOSNAM	14	-6

Find out and explain what the numbers in the score column mean.

Explain the meaning of words such as 'Birdie' and 'Bogey'.

Number patterns

Colin runs a small business.

He sells cans of home-made lemonade in packs of 8.

 How many cans are there in 2 packs?

How many cans in 3 packs?

The **multiples** of 8 are 8, 16, 24, . . .

Colin packs 8 cans like this:

4 cans along here

2 cans along here

4 and 2 are **factors** of 8.

 How else can he pack 8 cans using one layer?

What are the other factors of 8?

Colin decides to sell the lemonade in packs of 7 (one for each day of the week).

 How can 7 cans be packed in a rectangular box?

The only factors of 7 are 1 and 7. We say 7 is a **prime** number.

Colin runs a promotion. (Buy 8 – get 1 free!)

He sells the drinks in packs of 9.

 How can 9 cans be packed in a rectangular box?

9 is a **square number** because $3 \times 3 = 9$.

The **square root** of 9 is 3.

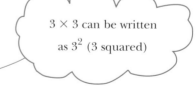 3×3 can be written as 3^2 (3 squared)

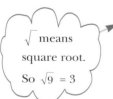 $\sqrt{}$ means square root. So $\sqrt{9} = 3$

Now Colin packs 8 cans like this

8 is a **cube number** because $2 \times 2 \times 2 = 8$.

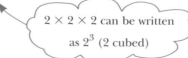 $2 \times 2 \times 2$ can be written as 2^3 (2 cubed)

1 List all the factors of

   a) 12   b) 16   c) 15   d) 28

   e) 25   f) 30   g) 48   h) 60

2 Find the value of

   a) 7^2 b) $\sqrt{64}$ c) 20^2 d) 5^3

   e) $\sqrt{100}$ f) 30^2 g) 3^3 h) $\sqrt{144}$

3 The first three primes are 2, 3 and 5. Write down the next five primes.

4 A pack contains 6 bags of crisps. How many bags of crisps are there in

   a) 2 packs?   b) 3 packs?   c) 5 packs?

5 20 cartons can be packed like this.

   a) List all the other ways of packing 20 cartons in a rectangular box.

   b) Now list all the factors of 20.

6 Two square cakes are made in tins which are 30 cm by 30 cm.

The chocolate cake is cut into 5 cm by 5 cm pieces.

   a) How many pieces is the chocolate cake divided into?

   b) Now the lemon cake is cut into 3 cm by 3 cm pieces.

      How many pieces does the lemon cake make?

Go to a pet shop or supermarket.

Look at the way tins of dog food are packed in boxes.

Why do you think they are packed like this?

How would you pack them?

Index notation

10×10 can be written 10^2 (10 squared).

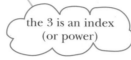

the 2 is an **index** (or power)

$10 \times 10 \times 10$ can be written 10^3 (10 cubed).

the 3 is an index (or power)

What is the value of 10^2?

What is the value of 10^3?

What do you think 10^4 means?

What is the value of 10^4?

Index notation is used so we don't have to write out

$$10 \times 10 \times 10 \times 10 \times 10 \times 10$$

How would you write this in index notation?

What is its value?

Standard form

Copy and complete this table.

4	4	4
4×10	4×10	40
$4 \times 10 \times 10$	4×10^2	400
$4 \times 10 \times 10 \times 10$		
$4 \times 10 \times 10 \times 10 \times 10$		
$4 \times 10 \times 10 \times 10 \times 10 \times 10$	4×10^5	400 000

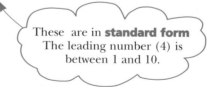

These are in **standard form**
The leading number (4) is between 1 and 10.

Here, the number is written in standard form and then worked out.

$$6 \times 10^3 = 6 \times 10 \times 10 \times 10 = 6000$$

The leading number is between 1 and 10

Here the number has been changed into standard form.

$$300\,000 = 3 \times 10 \times 10 \times 10 \times 10 \times 10 = 3 \times 10^5$$

The leading number is between 1 and 10

1 Work out the value of

a) 4^3 b) 2^5 c) 3^4 d) 2^6

e) 6^3 f) 6^4 g) 1.5^2 h) 2.5^3

2 In this question, the number is given in standard form. Work out the value of the number.

a) 5×10^2 b) 7×10^4 c) 8×10^3 d) 2×10^5

e) 6.5×10^2 f) 5.8×10^3 g) 2.4×10^6 h) 8.75×10^4

3 In this question, write the number in standard form.

a) 7000   b) 300   c) 90 000   d) 6000

e) 8600   f) 57 000   g) 750   h) 290 000

4 Using index notation, ten can be written as 10^1.
Write the following in index notation.

a) A hundred   b) A thousand   c) A million.

5 Most calculators have an $\boxed{X^y}$ key.

Find out how to use the $\boxed{X^y}$ key, and do question 1 again using this key.

Investigation

Look at this list of powers of 6.

$6^1 = 6$

$6^2 = 36$

$6^3 = 216$

$6^4 = 1296$

$6^5 = 7776$

$6^6 = 46\,656$

What do you notice about the last digit of these numbers?
Do any other numbers apart from 6 make a pattern like this?
Make a list like the one above for all the numbers less than 10 and see if you can spot any more patterns.

Look in a book containing lots of numbers, such as *The Guinness Book of Records*.

Find 4 very large numbers, and write them in standard form.

Calculators

Without using a calculator write down the value of 4×10^6.

Do the same for 4×10^{11}.

Now work out 4×10^{11} on your calculator, by pressing

$$4 \times 10 \times 10 \times 10 \times 10 \times 10 \times 10 \times 10 \times 10 \times 10 \times 10$$

What do you get?

Instead of showing 400 000 000 000 your calculator probably shows something like one of these:

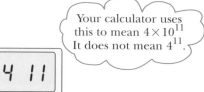

Your calculator uses this to mean 4×10^{11}. It does not mean 4^{11}.

Your calculator can only show a limited number of digits (probably 8 or 10).

It does not have enough space to display 400 000 000 000.

William is a tax inspector.

He wants to know the total number of hours of work people in Britain do in a year. He works it out like this:

One person works 40 hours a week for 50 weeks
In a year, one person works 40×50 = 2000 hours
There are about 30 000 000 workers in Britain
Total hours is 2000 × 30 000 000

He does this on a calculator and gets

His calculator uses this to mean 6×10^{10}

$6 \times 10^{10} = 6 \times 10\ 000\ 000\ 000 = 60\ 000\ 000\ 000$

60 billion hours!

1 Work out the value of the numbers displayed.

a)

7^{09}

b)

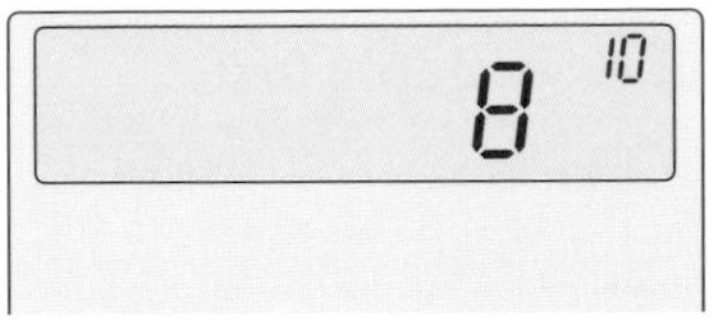

8^{10}

c)

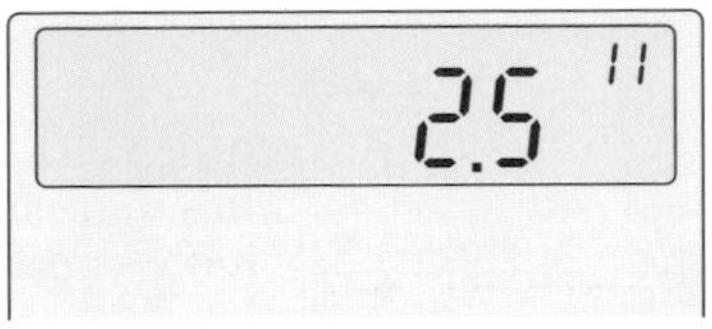

2.5^{11}

d)

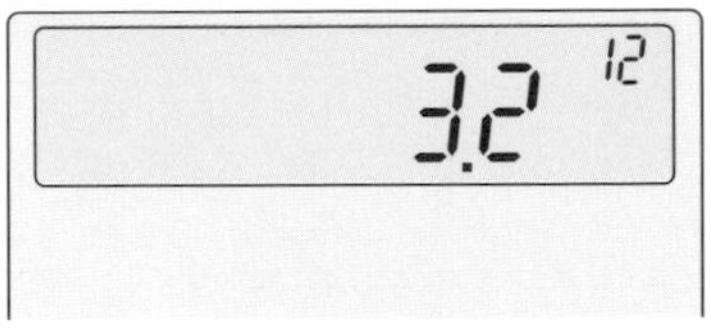

3.2^{12}

2 Work out the value of

a) 3 000 000 × 200 000

b) 80 000 000 × 50 000

c) 20 000 000 × 400 000

d) 5000 × 6 000 000

e) 25 000 × 600 000

f) 5 500 000 × 400 000

Investigation

Work out the powers of 3 starting with 3^2.

Stop when your calculator goes into standard form.

Work out the sum of the digits in each answer.

Write your results in a table like this.

Power of 3	Sum of the digits
$3^2 = 3 \times 3 = 9$	$9 = 9$
$3^3 = 3 \times 3 \times 3 = 27$	$2 + 7 = 9$

> To find the sum of the digits add them together.
> For 6561, $6 + 5 + 6 + 1 = 18$

a) Look at the answers in the first column.

   What do you notice about the last digits?

b) Look at the answers in the second column.

   What do you notice?

The Earth is believed to be 4500 million years old. How many seconds is this?

Brackets

 What is $1 + 2 \times 3$?

Did you add or multiply first?

John does it like this: Lisa does it like this:

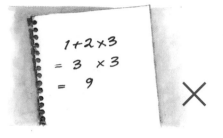

 Why is 7 *right and* 9 *wrong?*

Using brackets avoids confusion.

You always work out brackets first.

$(1 + 2) \times 3$ $1 + (2 \times 3)$

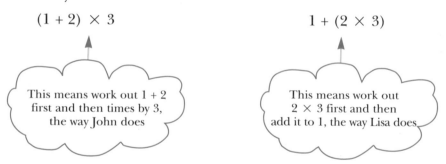

> This means work out $1 + 2$ first and then times by 3, the way John does

> This means work out 2×3 first and then add it to 1, the way Lisa does

You should always work out operations in this order:

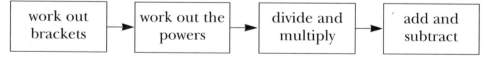

| work out brackets | → | work out the powers | → | divide and multiply | → | add and subtract |

This is how a scientific calculator works out $1 + 2 \times 3$:

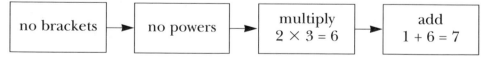

| no brackets | → | no powers | → | multiply $2 \times 3 = 6$ | → | add $1 + 6 = 7$ |

Using brackets, key in $1 + (2 \times 3)$ and check that you get 7.

Using brackets, key in $(1 + 2) \times 3$ and check that you get 9.

 What is $(20 - 8) \div 2$?

What is $20 - (8 \div 2)$?

What is $20 - 8 \div 2$?

1 Work out the value of

    a) $4 + (5 \times 3)$ b) $(4 + 5) \times 3$ c) $(11 - 2) \times 4$

    d) $11 - (2 \times 4)$ e) $2 \times (7 - 3)$ f) $(2 \times 7) - 3$

2 Work out the value of

    a) $5 + 3 \times 4$ b) $8 \times 3 - 1$ c) $12 \div 2 + 4$ d) $16 - 2 \times 3$

3 Work out the value of

    a) $(3 + 2) \times (4 - 1)$ b) $3 + (2 \times 4) - 1$

    c) $(5 \times 2) + (3 \times 4)$ d) $(20 \div 4) - 2$

4 Complete the following by using $+$, $-$, $\times$ or $\div$ in each box.

    You can use brackets as well to show which operation is done first.

    For example: $3 \ \square \ 4 \ \square \ 2 = 14$.

    One solution is $(3 + 4) \times 2 = 14$.

    Another is $(3 \times 4) + 2 = 14$.

> These brackets are not essential here

    a) $4 \square 5 \square 3 = 6$ b) $7 \square 5 \square 3 = 4$ c) $2 \square 6 \square 3 = 15$

    d) $5 \square 2 \square 2 = 14$ e) $3 \square 5 \square 1 = 12$ f) $3 \square 2 \square 2 = 8$

    g) $1 \square 6 \square 2 = 4$ h) $6 \square 6 \square 4 = 9$ i) $8 \square 2 \square 3 = 7$

    j) $10 \square 8 \square 2 = 9$

Investigation

Look at these calculations.

$$4 + 4 + \frac{4}{4} = 9 \qquad 4 - \frac{(4 + 4)}{4} = 2$$

> $\frac{4}{4} = 1$

> $\frac{4 + 4}{4} = \frac{8}{4} = 2$

$$(4 \times 4) + (4 \times 4) = 32$$

> $4 \times 4 = 16$

Each calculation uses exactly four 4s.

Using exactly four 4s invent 10 calculations of your own which give different answers.

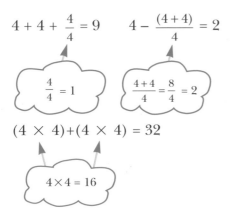

PRICES	
Fish	£1·60
Burger	£1·50
Veggie Burger	£1·50
Chips	·90

Buy a meal for your family or a group of friends. Write down the total cost using the signs $\times$, $+$, and ().

Write down the cost per person, if it is shared equally. You will need to use the $\div$ sign now as well.

Finishing off

Now that you have finished this chapter you should be able to

- ★ do calculations using length, mass, capacity, time and money

- ★ do calculations with negative amounts

- ★ work out multiples, factors, primes, squares, square roots and cubes

- ★ use index notation

- ★ work out a large number given in standard form on a calculator display

- ★ write a large number in standard form

- ★ decide which order to carry out operations in.

Use the questions in the next exercise to check that you understand everything.

Mixed exercise

1 Connor buys 5 pieces of curtain material each 120 cm long.

a) How many metres of curtain material does he buy?

b) A metre of material costs £4.50. How much does Connor pay?

c) The width of this material is $1\frac{1}{2}$ metres. What is this in inches? (Give your answer to the nearest inch.)

2 A container weighs 400 kg.

a) How much do 5 containers weigh?

b) Write this amount in tonnes.

c) A truck weighs 3.5 tonnes. It is loaded with 5 containers. What is the total weight of the truck and its load?

d) The truck costs thirty thousand six hundred and nine pounds. Write this cost in figures.

3 A water tank has a capacity of 200 gallons. How much is this in litres?

4 Julie catches the 1738 train from York. She arrives in Edinburgh at 2004. How long did the journey take? (Give your answer in hours and minutes.)

5 A bookshop has two branches, A and B.

This table shows the number of French dictionaries sold over a 4-month period.

	April	May	June	July	Total
Branch A	7	8	7	6	
Branch B	5		6		
Total	12	15		11	

Copy the table and work out the missing entries.

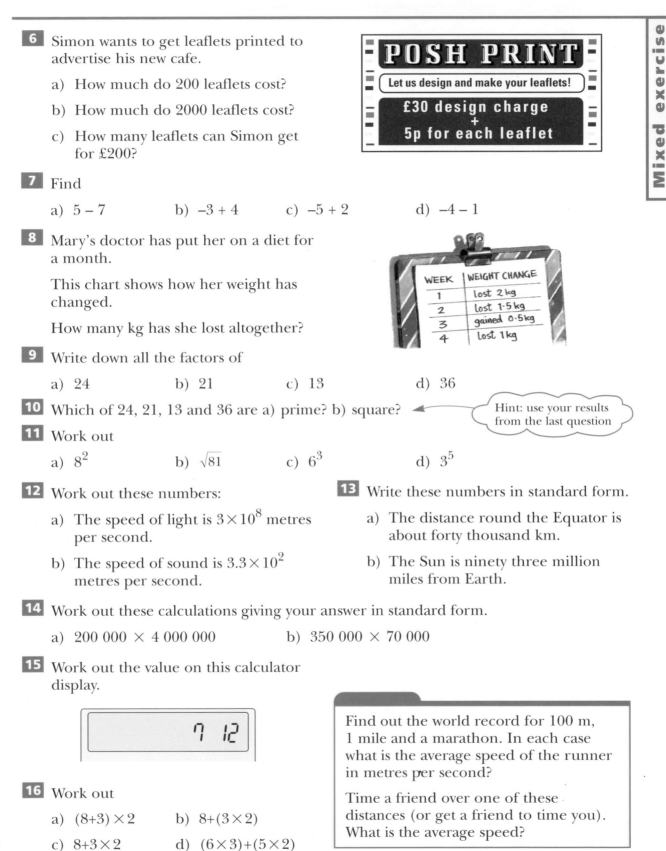

6 Simon wants to get leaflets printed to advertise his new cafe.

a) How much do 200 leaflets cost?

b) How much do 2000 leaflets cost?

c) How many leaflets can Simon get for £200?

POSH PRINT

Let us design and make your leaflets!

£30 design charge
+
5p for each leaflet

7 Find

a) $5 - 7$ b) $-3 + 4$ c) $-5 + 2$ d) $-4 - 1$

8 Mary's doctor has put her on a diet for a month.

This chart shows how her weight has changed.

How many kg has she lost altogether?

WEEK	WEIGHT CHANGE
1	lost 2 kg
2	lost 1·5 kg
3	gained 0·5 kg
4	lost 1 kg

9 Write down all the factors of

a) 24   b) 21   c) 13   d) 36

10 Which of 24, 21, 13 and 36 are a) prime? b) square?

Hint: use your results from the last question

11 Work out

a) 8^2 b) $\sqrt{81}$ c) 6^3 d) 3^5

12 Work out these numbers:

a) The speed of light is 3×10^8 metres per second.

b) The speed of sound is 3.3×10^2 metres per second.

13 Write these numbers in standard form.

a) The distance round the Equator is about forty thousand km.

b) The Sun is ninety three million miles from Earth.

14 Work out these calculations giving your answer in standard form.

a) $200\,000 \times 4\,000\,000$ b) $350\,000 \times 70\,000$

15 Work out the value on this calculator display.

7 12

16 Work out

a) $(8+3) \times 2$ b) $8+(3 \times 2)$

c) $8+3 \times 2$ d) $(6 \times 3)+(5 \times 2)$

Find out the world record for 100 m, 1 mile and a marathon. In each case what is the average speed of the runner in metres per second?

Time a friend over one of these distances (or get a friend to time you). What is the average speed?

Two

Measuring and drawing

Use the following questions to check that you still remember these topics.

Reminder

There are two main types of scale used in maps and drawings.

Means 1 cm on the map stands for 2 km in real life

1 cm:2 km

1:50 000

Means 1 cm stands for 50 000 cm (or 500 m), 1 mile stands for 50 000 miles and so on

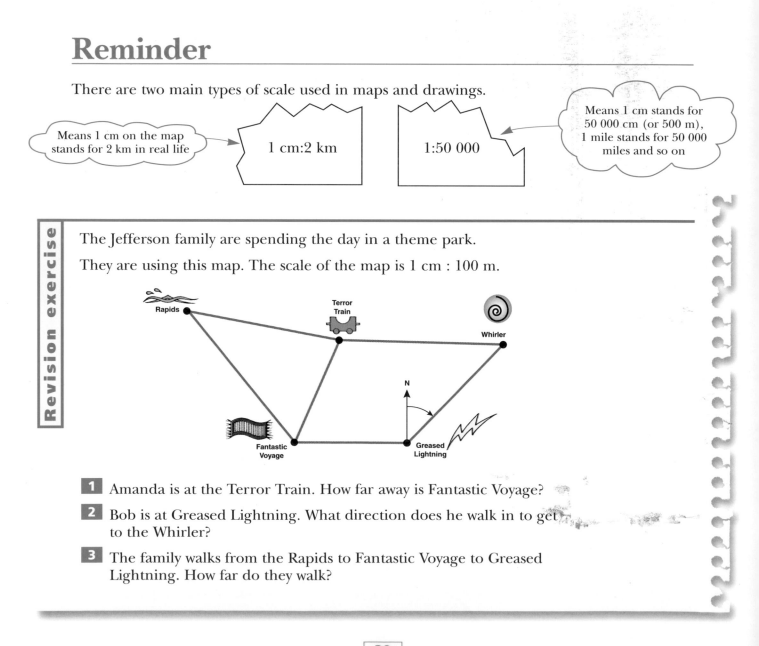

Revision exercise

The Jefferson family are spending the day in a theme park.

They are using this map. The scale of the map is 1 cm : 100 m.

1 Amanda is at the Terror Train. How far away is Fantastic Voyage?

2 Bob is at Greased Lightning. What direction does he walk in to get to the Whirler?

3 The family walks from the Rapids to Fantastic Voyage to Greased Lightning. How far do they walk?

4 Use a protractor or angle measurer to measure these angles.

a)

b)

c)

d)

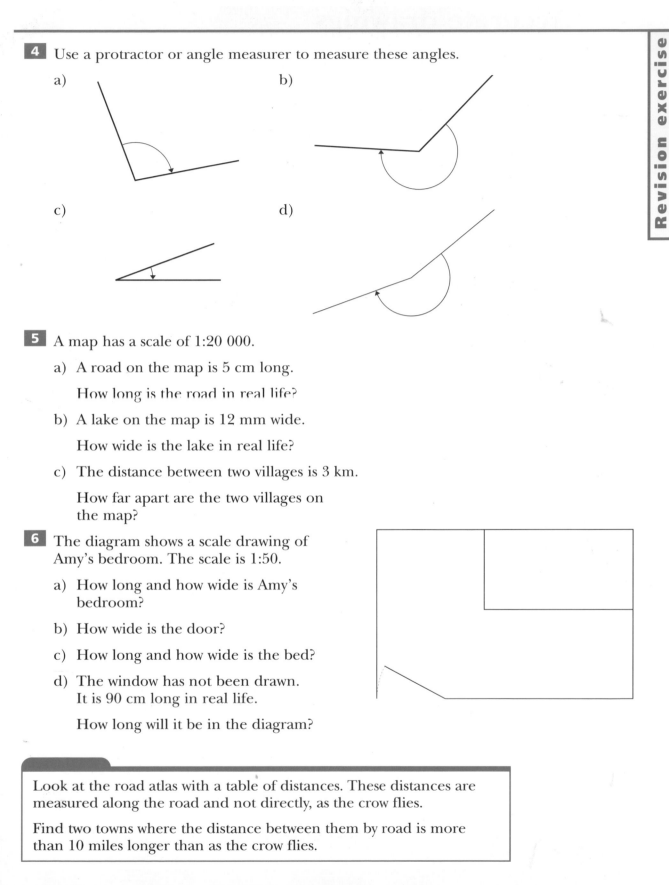

5 A map has a scale of 1:20 000.

a) A road on the map is 5 cm long.

How long is the road in real life?

b) A lake on the map is 12 mm wide.

How wide is the lake in real life?

c) The distance between two villages is 3 km.

How far apart are the two villages on the map?

6 The diagram shows a scale drawing of Amy's bedroom. The scale is 1:50.

a) How long and how wide is Amy's bedroom?

b) How wide is the door?

c) How long and how wide is the bed?

d) The window has not been drawn. It is 90 cm long in real life.

How long will it be in the diagram?

Look at the road atlas with a table of distances. These distances are measured along the road and not directly, as the crow flies.

Find two towns where the distance between them by road is more than 10 miles longer than as the crow flies.

Accurate drawings

Engineers, architects and manufacturers must be able to draw accurate diagrams, either full size or to scale.

They work very accurately to make sure that the finished product fits together properly and is safe to use.

 When have you worked with accurate drawings?

Equipment you will need

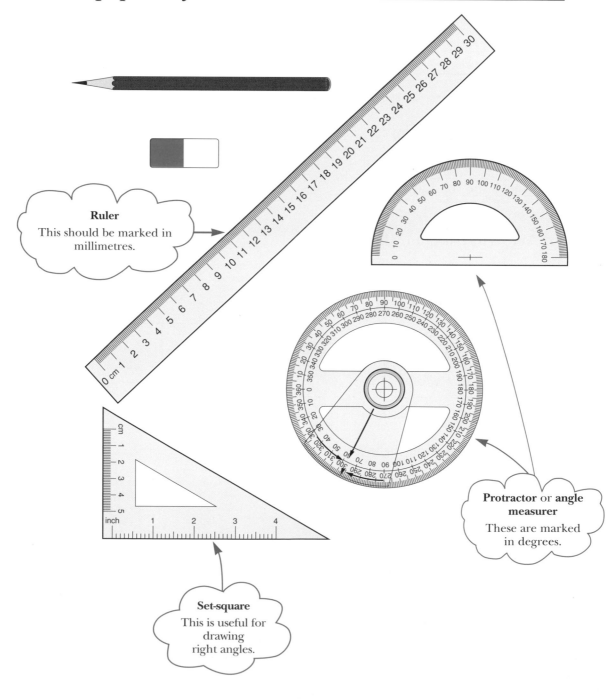

Ruler
This should be marked in millimetres.

Protractor or **angle measurer**
These are marked in degrees.

Set-square
This is useful for drawing right angles.

Use plain paper for this exercise.

1 You are going to draw a rectangle 10 cm long and 4 cm wide.

a) Use your ruler to draw a line exactly 10 cm long.

b) Put the set-square at one end of the line and use it to draw a line at right angles to your first line.

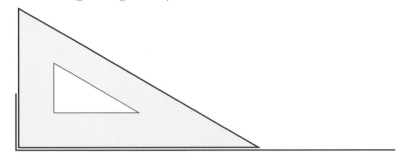

c) Take the set-square away and use a ruler to extend the line until it is exactly 4 cm long.

Then use the set-square again to draw another line at the other end of the original line, also 4 cm long.

d) Join up the ends of the two 4 cm lines to make the rectangle. Check that this line is 10 cm long.

2 a) Draw a rectangle 5 cm long and 8 cm wide.

b) Measure the diagonal of the rectangle.

Draw a scale drawing of a tennis court or football pitch.

More shapes

Gary is an architect.

He needs to draw this triangle accurately.

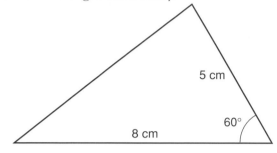

This is how he does it.

He draws a line exactly 8 cm long.

He puts his protractor so that the centre is on the right-hand side of his line and the zero line is exactly on top of the line he has just drawn.

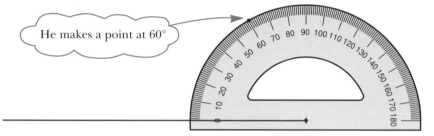

He makes a point at 60°

He takes the protractor away and joins up the point and the end of the line.

He extends the line until it is 5 cm long.

Then he joins up the two lines.

He measures this line – it is exactly 7 cm

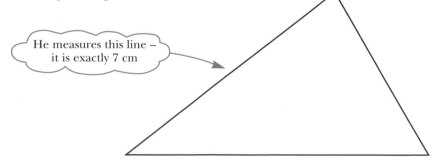

Now do this yourself.
Check that you get 7 cm as well.

1 In this question, you will draw a triangle when you know the length of one side and the sizes of two angles.

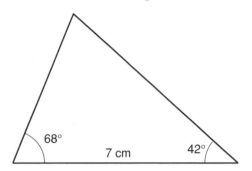

a) Draw a line exactly 7 cm long.

b) Mark off an angle of 42° at the right-hand end of the line.

   Join this end of the line to your mark.

c) Mark off an angle of 68° at the left-hand end of the 7 cm line.
   Join this end of the line to your mark.

d) Extend both lines if necessary until they meet.

e) Measure your lines.

2 This diagram shows three of the fields at Springdale Farm.

The diagram is not drawn to scale but some of the lengths and angles are marked on.

a) Make an accurate drawing of the three fields, using a scale of 1 cm to 20 m. (Hint: start by drawing the line which is 100 m long.)

b) The farmer is thinking of making the three fields into one big field. He wants to know how far it would be across the whole field from corner A to corner B. Measure the distance on your scale drawing, and work out what the distance would be in real life.

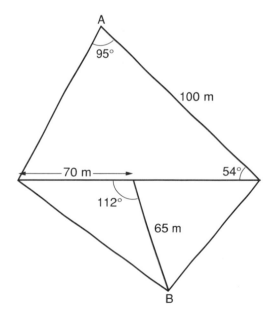

Give 5 examples of where you see triangles in everyday life.

In each case, roughly how long are the sides of the triangle?

Using bearings

An aeroplane is flying from London to Manchester.

The pilot needs to know exactly what direction to take.

She can do this by measuring the angle on the map between the direction she needs to fly in and a line going north from London.

The angle is measured clockwise from the North line.

North

Manchester

This is the angle the pilot needs to measure

London

Use an angle measurer to measure this angle.

You should find that it is 330 degrees.

This angle is called the **bearing** of Manchester from London.

Remember that bearings are always measured clockwise from North.

Bearings are always written with three figures.

A bearing of 62° is written as 062°.

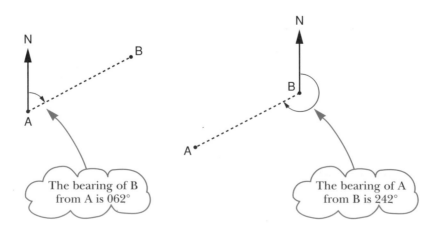

The bearing of B from A is 062°

The bearing of A from B is 242°

1 A, B, C and D are 4 ships.

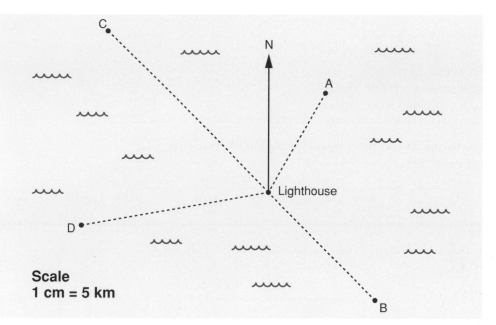

Scale
1 cm = 5 km

a) Measure the bearing of each of the ships from the lighthouse.

b) Find the distance of each ship from the lighthouse.

2 This diagram shows three towns, A, B and C.

Measure the bearing of

a) A from B   b) B from A

c) A from C   d) C from A

e) B from C   f) C from B

g) What do you notice about each pair of bearings?

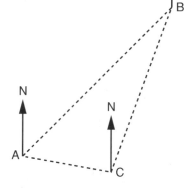

3 Andrew and Ranjit are on a hike in the hills.

They find that a nearby hill, Mill Crag, is on a bearing of 158°.

They walk for 4 km north-east and then find that Mill Crag is on a bearing of 205°. Make a scale drawing of their journey, using a scale of 1:50 000.

Use your drawing to find out how far they are from Mill Crag at each of the points where they take a bearing.

Plan a walk through open country.

Finishing off

> **Now that you have finished this chapter you should be able to**
>
> ★ draw, full size or to scale, accurate drawings of shapes such as rectangles and triangles, using a ruler and protractor or angle measurer
>
> ★ use three-figure bearings.

Use the questions in the next exercise to check that you understand everything.

Mixed exercise

1 Make accurate full size drawings of the triangles ABC and XYZ shown below.

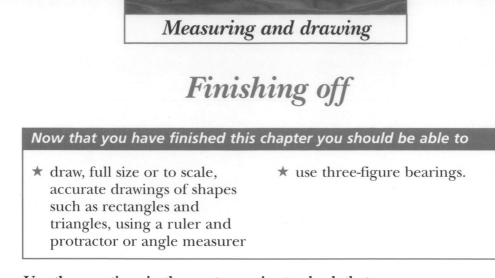

a) Measure the length of side AB on your first drawing.

b) Measure the lengths of sides X Z and YZ on your second drawing.

2 a) Make a scale drawing of the field PQRST shown here, using a scale of 1:2500.

(Hint: start by drawing the rectangle OPQR, then add the triangle OPT, then the triangle RST.)

b) Measure the lengths of sides ST and TP on your drawing.

c) What are the lengths of sides ST and TP of the real field?

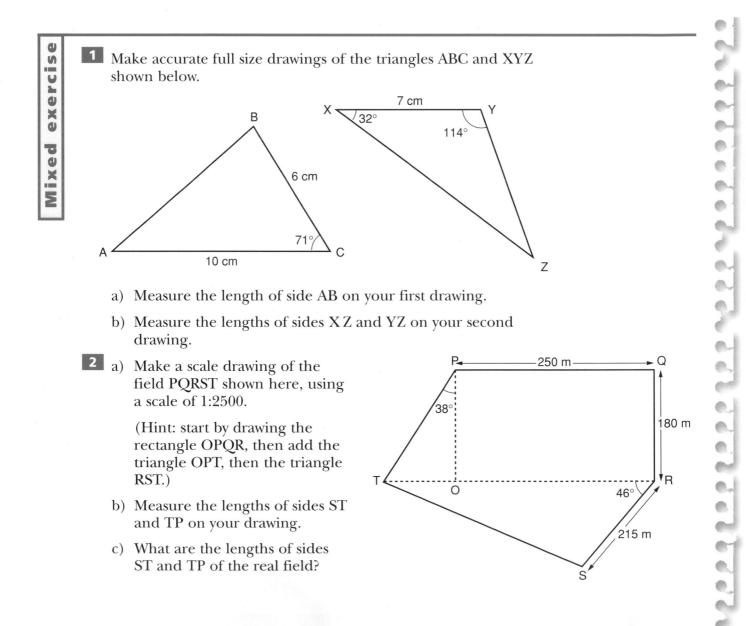

3 The map shows some ferry routes across the English Channel.

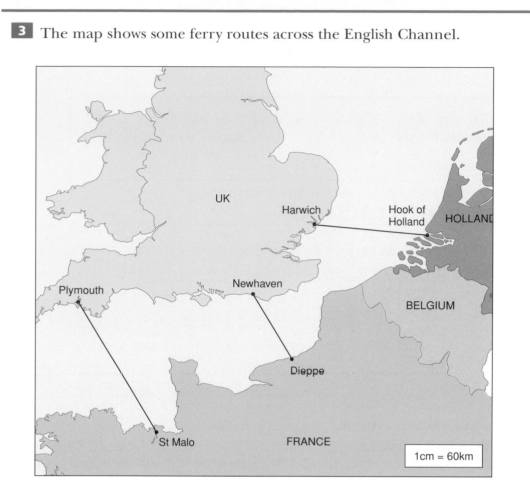

1cm = 60km

a) What bearing must a ferry sail on to travel from

   (i)   Plymouth to St Malo?

   (ii) Dieppe to Newhaven?

   (iii) Harwich to Hook of Holland?

b) How far is each of the journeys above in real life?

Measure the length and width of your living room.

Make a scale drawing of the room on squared paper. Put in the positions of the doors and windows, and any fixed furniture.

Make drawings on squared paper, using the same scale, of the furniture in the room. Cut them out and use them to design a new arrangement for your living room.

When you are happy with your design, stick it down.

This is the way designers work in real life.

Three
Fractions

★ The early part of this chapter revises topics from Book 1.

★ Make sure you really understand them before you go on to the new work.

Equivalent fractions

What fraction is shaded in each of these diagrams?

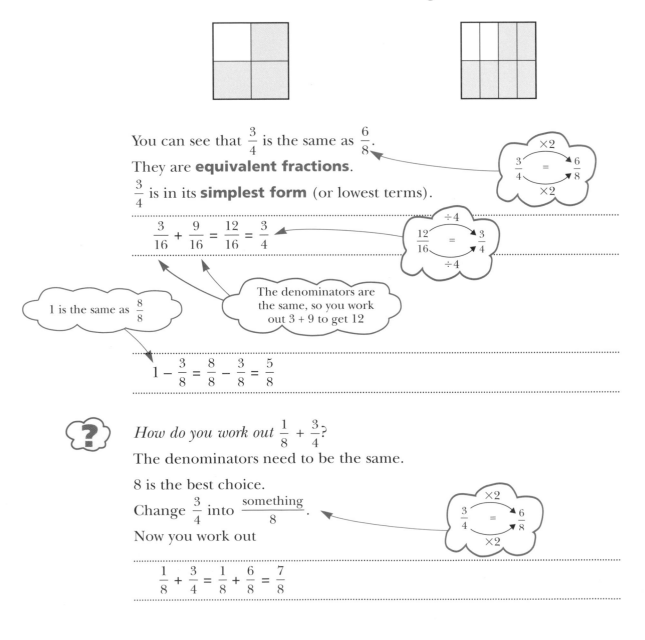

You can see that $\frac{3}{4}$ is the same as $\frac{6}{8}$.

They are **equivalent fractions**.

$\frac{3}{4}$ is in its **simplest form** (or lowest terms).

$$\frac{3}{16} + \frac{9}{16} = \frac{12}{16} = \frac{3}{4}$$

1 is the same as $\frac{8}{8}$

The denominators are the same, so you work out $3 + 9$ to get 12

$$1 - \frac{3}{8} = \frac{8}{8} - \frac{3}{8} = \frac{5}{8}$$

How do you work out $\frac{1}{8} + \frac{3}{4}$?

The denominators need to be the same.

8 is the best choice.

Change $\frac{3}{4}$ into $\frac{\text{something}}{8}$.

Now you work out

$$\frac{1}{8} + \frac{3}{4} = \frac{1}{8} + \frac{6}{8} = \frac{7}{8}$$

1 Work out a single fraction for

a) $\frac{5}{16} + \frac{9}{16}$ b) $\frac{7}{8} - \frac{3}{8}$ c) $1 - \frac{2}{5}$ d) $1 - \frac{11}{16}$

2 Find the missing number:

a) $\frac{1}{2} = \frac{?}{8}$ b) $\frac{3}{5} = \frac{?}{10}$ c) $\frac{2}{3} = \frac{4}{?}$ d) $\frac{1}{4} = \frac{?}{12}$

e) $\frac{20}{30} = \frac{2}{?}$ f) $\frac{5}{8} = \frac{?}{16}$ g) $\frac{3}{4} = \frac{?}{100}$ h) $\frac{3}{10} = \frac{?}{100}$

3 Fill in the missing numbers:

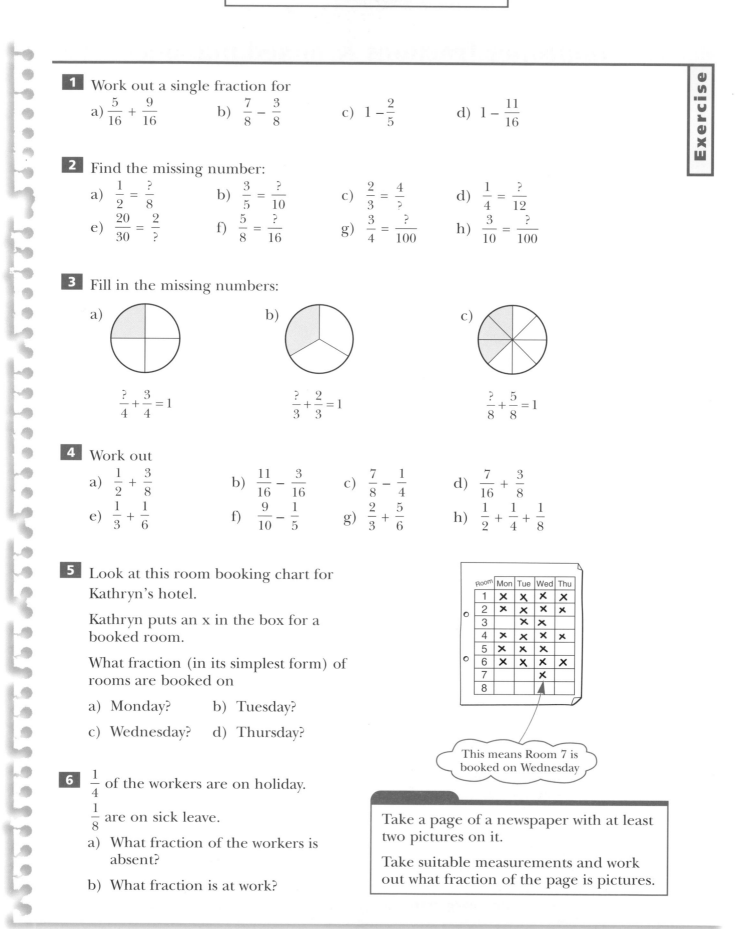

a)

$\frac{?}{4} + \frac{3}{4} = 1$

b)

$\frac{?}{3} + \frac{2}{3} = 1$

c)

$\frac{?}{8} + \frac{5}{8} = 1$

4 Work out

a) $\frac{1}{2} + \frac{3}{8}$ b) $\frac{11}{16} - \frac{3}{16}$ c) $\frac{7}{8} - \frac{1}{4}$ d) $\frac{7}{16} + \frac{3}{8}$

e) $\frac{1}{3} + \frac{1}{6}$ f) $\frac{9}{10} - \frac{1}{5}$ g) $\frac{2}{3} + \frac{5}{6}$ h) $\frac{1}{2} + \frac{1}{4} + \frac{1}{8}$

5 Look at this room booking chart for Kathryn's hotel.

Kathryn puts an x in the box for a booked room.

What fraction (in its simplest form) of rooms are booked on

a) Monday? b) Tuesday?

c) Wednesday? d) Thursday?

Room	Mon	Tue	Wed	Thu
1	✗	✗	✗	✗
2	✗	✗	✗	✗
3		✗	✗	
4	✗	✗	✗	✗
5	✗	✗	✗	
6	✗	✗	✗	✗
7			✗	
8				

This means Room 7 is booked on Wednesday

6 $\frac{1}{4}$ of the workers are on holiday.

$\frac{1}{8}$ are on sick leave.

a) What fraction of the workers is absent?

b) What fraction is at work?

Take a page of a newspaper with at least two pictures on it.

Take suitable measurements and work out what fraction of the page is pictures.

Improper fractions & mixed numbers

George and Marie are counsellors.

They have these afternoon appointments.

How long is George booked for?

George has 7 appointments, each $\frac{1}{2}$ hour long.

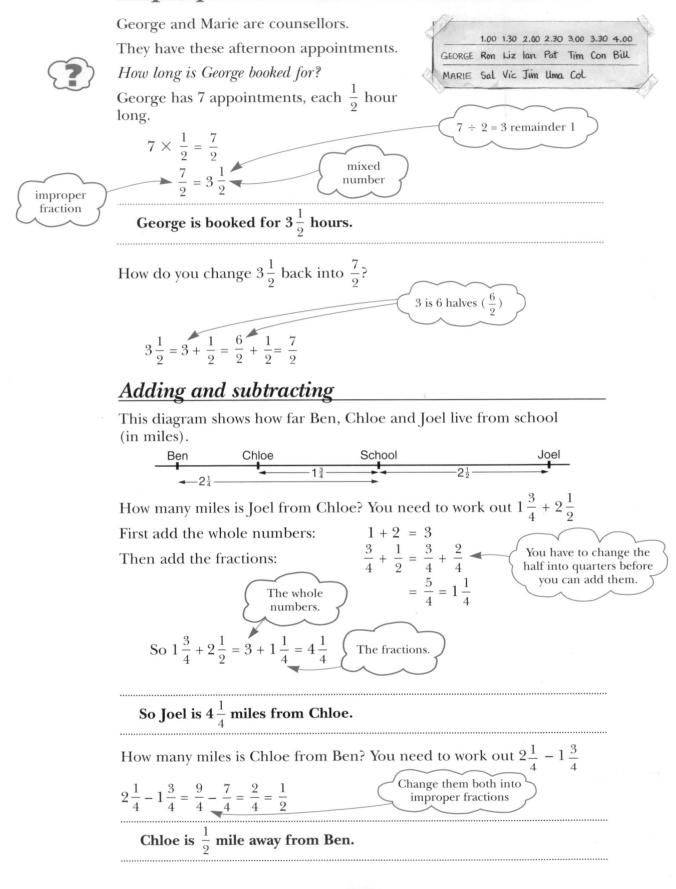

	1.00	1.30	2.00	2.30	3.00	3.30	4.00
GEORGE	Ron	Liz	Ian	Pat	Tim	Con	Bill
MARIE	Sal	Vic	Jim	Uma	Col		

$7 \times \frac{1}{2} = \frac{7}{2}$

$\frac{7}{2} = 3\frac{1}{2}$

7 ÷ 2 = 3 remainder 1

mixed number

improper fraction

George is booked for $3\frac{1}{2}$ hours.

How do you change $3\frac{1}{2}$ back into $\frac{7}{2}$?

3 is 6 halves ($\frac{6}{2}$)

$3\frac{1}{2} = 3 + \frac{1}{2} = \frac{6}{2} + \frac{1}{2} = \frac{7}{2}$

Adding and subtracting

This diagram shows how far Ben, Chloe and Joel live from school (in miles).

Ben — Chloe — School — Joel

$2\frac{1}{4}$ $1\frac{3}{4}$ $2\frac{1}{2}$

How many miles is Joel from Chloe? You need to work out $1\frac{3}{4} + 2\frac{1}{2}$

First add the whole numbers: $1 + 2 = 3$

Then add the fractions: $\frac{3}{4} + \frac{1}{2} = \frac{3}{4} + \frac{2}{4}$

$= \frac{5}{4} = 1\frac{1}{4}$

You have to change the half into quarters before you can add them.

The whole numbers.

So $1\frac{3}{4} + 2\frac{1}{2} = 3 + 1\frac{1}{4} = 4\frac{1}{4}$

The fractions.

So Joel is $4\frac{1}{4}$ miles from Chloe.

How many miles is Chloe from Ben? You need to work out $2\frac{1}{4} - 1\frac{3}{4}$

$2\frac{1}{4} - 1\frac{3}{4} = \frac{9}{4} - \frac{7}{4} = \frac{2}{4} = \frac{1}{2}$

Change them both into improper fractions

Chloe is $\frac{1}{2}$ mile away from Ben.

1 Change the improper fraction to a mixed number:

a) $\dfrac{11}{8}$ b) $\dfrac{7}{3}$ c) $\dfrac{11}{2}$ d) $\dfrac{20}{4}$

2 Change the mixed number to an improper fraction:

a) $3\dfrac{1}{4}$ b) $2\dfrac{3}{8}$ c) $1\dfrac{7}{16}$ d) $5\dfrac{3}{4}$

3 Work out

a) $2\dfrac{7}{8} + \dfrac{5}{8}$ b) $1\dfrac{1}{2} + 3\dfrac{5}{8}$ c) $2\dfrac{3}{4} - 1\dfrac{7}{16}$ d) $4 - \dfrac{3}{8}$

e) $4\dfrac{1}{4} - 2\dfrac{5}{8}$ f) $3\dfrac{7}{16} + 2\dfrac{13}{16}$ g) $5 - 3\dfrac{5}{8}$ h) $3\dfrac{5}{16} + 4\dfrac{7}{8}$

4 This map shows a canal and the distances between five barges, A, B, C, D and E (in miles).

$$\underset{A}{\bullet}\quad\overset{2\frac{1}{2}}{\rule{4cm}{0.4pt}}\quad\underset{B}{\bullet}\quad\overset{1\frac{1}{4}}{\rule{2cm}{0.4pt}}\quad\underset{C}{\bullet}\quad\overset{1\frac{3}{4}}{\rule{3cm}{0.4pt}}\quad\underset{D}{\bullet}\quad\overset{1\frac{1}{2}}{\rule{3cm}{0.4pt}}\quad\underset{E}{\bullet}$$

What is the distance from

a) B to D? b) A to C? c) C to E? d) A to E?

5 A pack of cherryade is made up of 12 cans. Each can contains one third of a litre. How many litres of cherryade does the pack contain?

6 On Wednesday morning, Dr Ling sees 7 people for a quarter of an hour each.

a) How long does it take her?

b) Dr Ling's $2\dfrac{3}{4}$ hour afternoon session is fully booked. Each patient has a quarter of an hour.

How many patients does she see in the session?

Look at the way square cakes are cut up in cafes and shops. Show 3 different ways of cutting a square cake into
a) 4 equal pieces
b) 8 equal pieces
c) 6 equal pieces.

Fraction of a quantity

1 in 3 workers lose jobs

There are 180 workers in the factory.

How many lose their jobs?

1 in 3 is the same as $\frac{1}{3}$.

You find $\frac{1}{3}$ of 180 by working out $180 \div 3 = 60$.

$\frac{1}{3}$ of 180
is the same as
$\frac{1}{3} \times 180$
or $\frac{1}{3} \times \frac{180}{1}$

180 workers — divide by 3 — Lose jobs / Keep jobs

Each third is 60.

So 60 workers lose their jobs.

How many still have jobs?

What fraction is this?

The next week the local paper has the headline

3/4 of job losers offered new work

There were 60 job losers.

How many are offered new work?

You find $\frac{3}{4}$ of 60 like this:

First you find $\frac{1}{4}$ of 60 by working out $60 \div 4 = 15$.

Now multiply this by 3 to get *three* quarters, $15 \times 3 = 45$.

$\frac{3}{4}$ of 60
is the same as
$\frac{3}{4} \times 60$
or $\frac{3}{4} \times \frac{60}{1}$

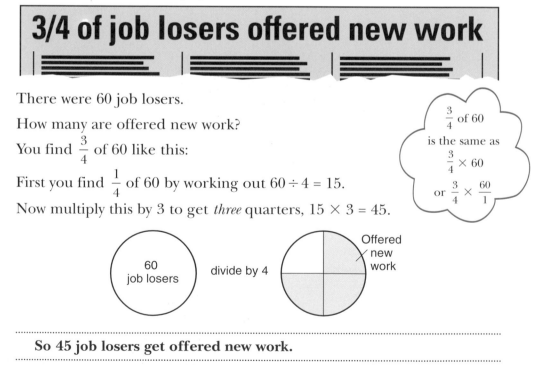

60 job losers — divide by 4 — Offered new work

So 45 job losers get offered new work.

How many do not get a new job?

What fraction of the job losers is this?

1 Work out

a) $\frac{1}{2}$ of 100

b) $\frac{1}{4}$ of 100

c) $\frac{1}{3}$ of 150

d) $\frac{3}{4}$ of 20

e) $\frac{2}{3}$ of 90

f) $\frac{2}{5}$ of 140

2 Janine goes shopping for a pair of shoes.

How much does Janine save if she buys these shoes in the sale?

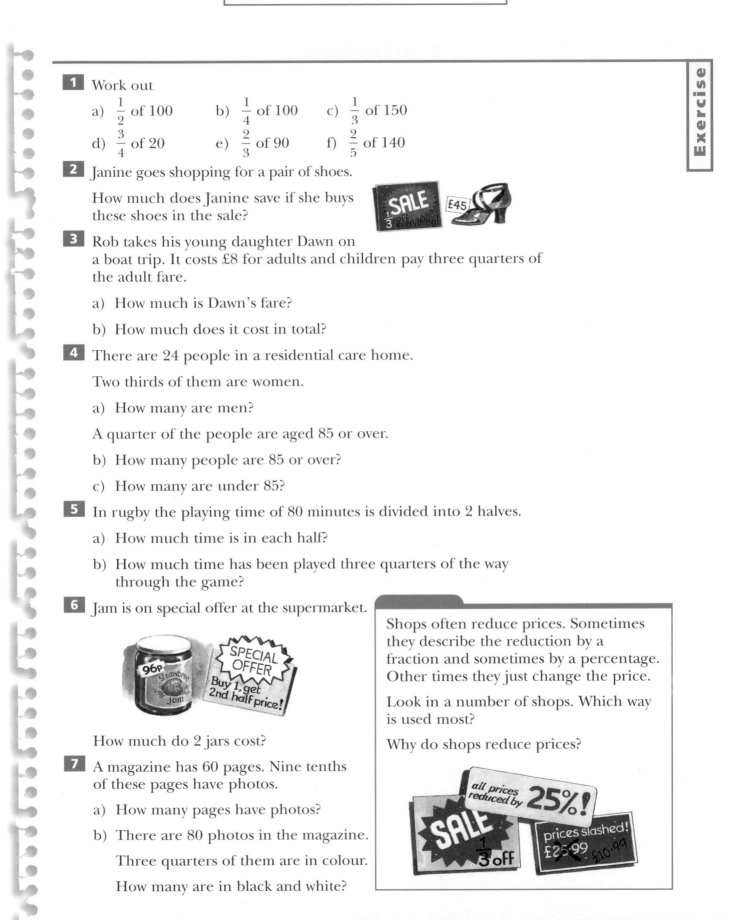

3 Rob takes his young daughter Dawn on a boat trip. It costs £8 for adults and children pay three quarters of the adult fare.

a) How much is Dawn's fare?

b) How much does it cost in total?

4 There are 24 people in a residential care home.

Two thirds of them are women.

a) How many are men?

A quarter of the people are aged 85 or over.

b) How many people are 85 or over?

c) How many are under 85?

5 In rugby the playing time of 80 minutes is divided into 2 halves.

a) How much time is in each half?

b) How much time has been played three quarters of the way through the game?

6 Jam is on special offer at the supermarket.

How much do 2 jars cost?

Shops often reduce prices. Sometimes they describe the reduction by a fraction and sometimes by a percentage. Other times they just change the price.

Look in a number of shops. Which way is used most?

Why do shops reduce prices?

7 A magazine has 60 pages. Nine tenths of these pages have photos.

a) How many pages have photos?

b) There are 80 photos in the magazine.

Three quarters of them are in colour.

How many are in black and white?

Finishing off

Now that you have finished this chapter you should be able to

★ find equivalent fractions and simplest forms

★ add and subtract fractions

★ change improper fractions and mixed numbers

★ find a fraction of a quantity.

Use the questions in the next exercise to check that you understand everything.

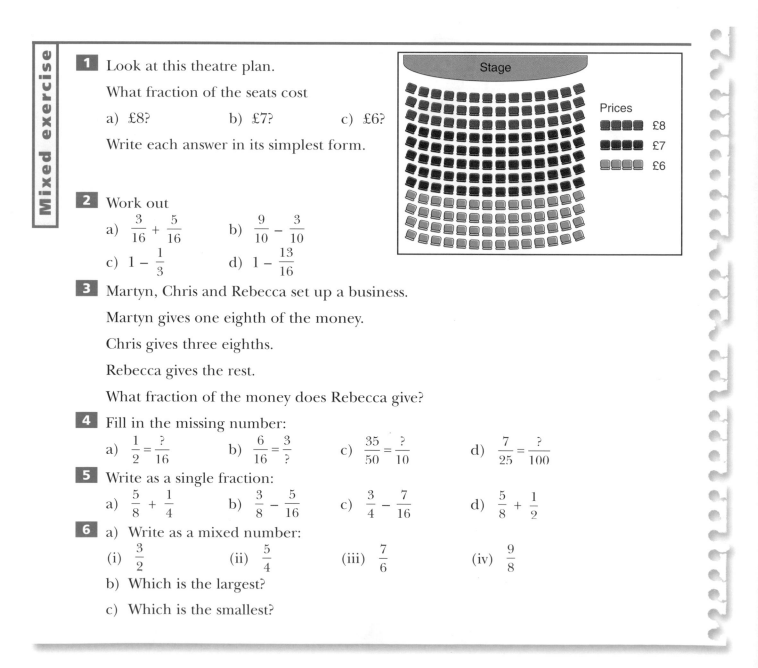

Mixed exercise

1 Look at this theatre plan.

What fraction of the seats cost

a) £8? b) £7? c) £6?

Write each answer in its simplest form.

Stage

Prices

£8

£7

£6

2 Work out

a) $\dfrac{3}{16} + \dfrac{5}{16}$ b) $\dfrac{9}{10} - \dfrac{3}{10}$

c) $1 - \dfrac{1}{3}$ d) $1 - \dfrac{13}{16}$

3 Martyn, Chris and Rebecca set up a business.

Martyn gives one eighth of the money.

Chris gives three eighths.

Rebecca gives the rest.

What fraction of the money does Rebecca give?

4 Fill in the missing number:

a) $\dfrac{1}{2} = \dfrac{?}{16}$ b) $\dfrac{6}{16} = \dfrac{3}{?}$ c) $\dfrac{35}{50} = \dfrac{?}{10}$ d) $\dfrac{7}{25} = \dfrac{?}{100}$

5 Write as a single fraction:

a) $\dfrac{5}{8} + \dfrac{1}{4}$ b) $\dfrac{3}{8} - \dfrac{5}{16}$ c) $\dfrac{3}{4} - \dfrac{7}{16}$ d) $\dfrac{5}{8} + \dfrac{1}{2}$

6 a) Write as a mixed number:

(i) $\dfrac{3}{2}$ (ii) $\dfrac{5}{4}$ (iii) $\dfrac{7}{6}$ (iv) $\dfrac{9}{8}$

b) Which is the largest?

c) Which is the smallest?

7 Write as an improper fraction:

a) $5\frac{1}{2}$
b) $2\frac{5}{6}$
c) $1\frac{7}{16}$
d) $4\frac{3}{8}$

8 This map shows three local beauty spots.

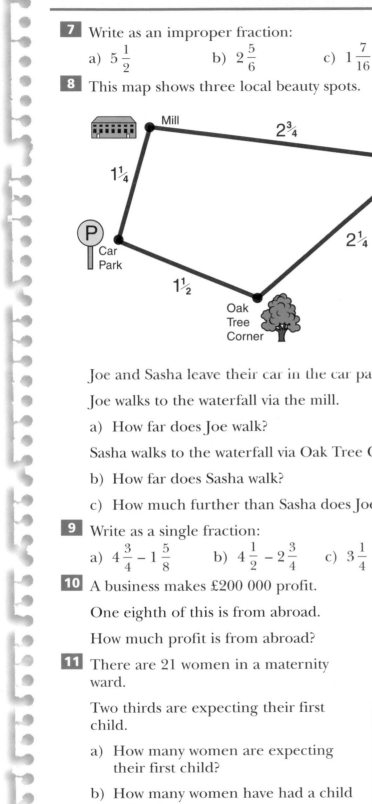

Joe and Sasha leave their car in the car park.

Joe walks to the waterfall via the mill.

a) How far does Joe walk?

Sasha walks to the waterfall via Oak Tree Corner.

b) How far does Sasha walk?

c) How much further than Sasha does Joe walk?

9 Write as a single fraction:

a) $4\frac{3}{4} - 1\frac{5}{8}$
b) $4\frac{1}{2} - 2\frac{3}{4}$
c) $3\frac{1}{4} + 4\frac{9}{16}$
d) $2\frac{11}{16} + 3\frac{5}{8}$

10 A business makes £200 000 profit.

One eighth of this is from abroad.

How much profit is from abroad?

11 There are 21 women in a maternity ward.

Two thirds are expecting their first child.

a) How many women are expecting their first child?

b) How many women have had a child before?

Look at a number of different newspapers. For each one, say how many pages are sport and what fraction this is of the whole paper.

Which papers have the highest and lowest fractions of sport?

Angles and shapes

Before you start this chapter, you should

★ be able to measure angles accurately

★ know that there are 360° in a whole turn.

Angles round a point and on a line

Measure the angle at the centre of each piece of pizza.

For each pizza, add up the angles you have measured.

What do you notice?

 You should have found that

Angles that fit round a point add up to 360°.

This works because there are 360° in a whole turn.

The number of degrees in half a turn is 180° (half of 360°).

An angle which is half a turn makes a straight line.

If several angles fit together to make a straight line, the angles must add up to 180°.

> half a turn or 180°

Angles that fit on a straight line add up to 180°.

You can use these rules when you are working out angles in a diagram, without measuring them.

> This must be 96° because
> 100 + 164 + 96 = 360

> Work this out as
> 100 + 164 = 264
> 360 − 264 = 96

> Work this out as 180 − 48 = 132
> The angle is 132°

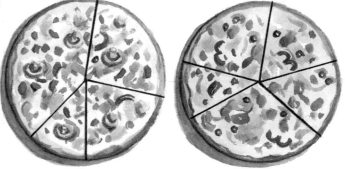

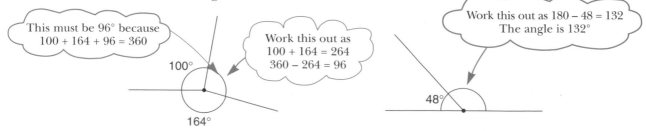

100°

164°

48°

1 Work out the angle marked with a letter in each of the diagrams. The diagrams are not drawn the correct size, so you must use the rules on the opposite page.

If you measure them, you will get the wrong answers!

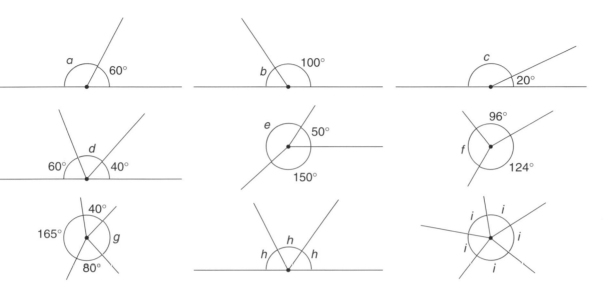

2 I dropped three identical plates and they each broke into several pieces. Work out which pieces fit together to make each plate.

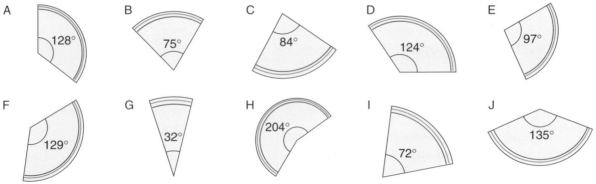

Try out this puzzle on your friends.

Draw 3 identical circles and cut each one into 3 pieces.

Make sure you cut the pieces from the centre of the circle, like the plates in question 2.

Now mix all the pieces up, and ask your friends to put the circles back together.

How long do they take?

Parallel lines

A trellis like this is often used in gardens.

It is made of two sets of parallel lines.

(Parallel lines are lines that go in the same direction and never meet.)

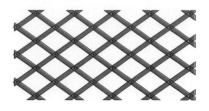

Here is a larger diagram of part of the trellis with some of the angles marked with letters.

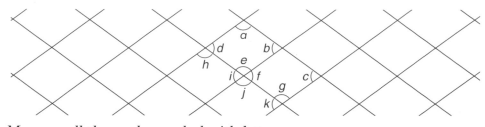

Measure all the angles marked with letters.

Which ones are the same as each other?

Find some rules for working out which angles are the same.

The rules

You may have found the rules below.

Where two lines cross, the angles opposite each other are equal. These are opposite angles.

Where a line crosses two parallel lines, these two angles are equal. These are corresponding angles. Look for the shape like a letter F.

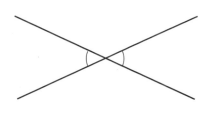

Parallel lines are shown with arrows

Where a line crosses two parallel lines, these two angles are equal. These are alternate angles. Look for the shape of a letter Z.

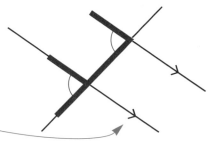

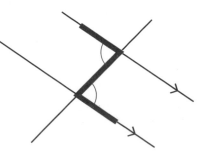

1 a) Which angles in the diagram are the same as angle *x*?

b) Which angles are the same as angle *y*?

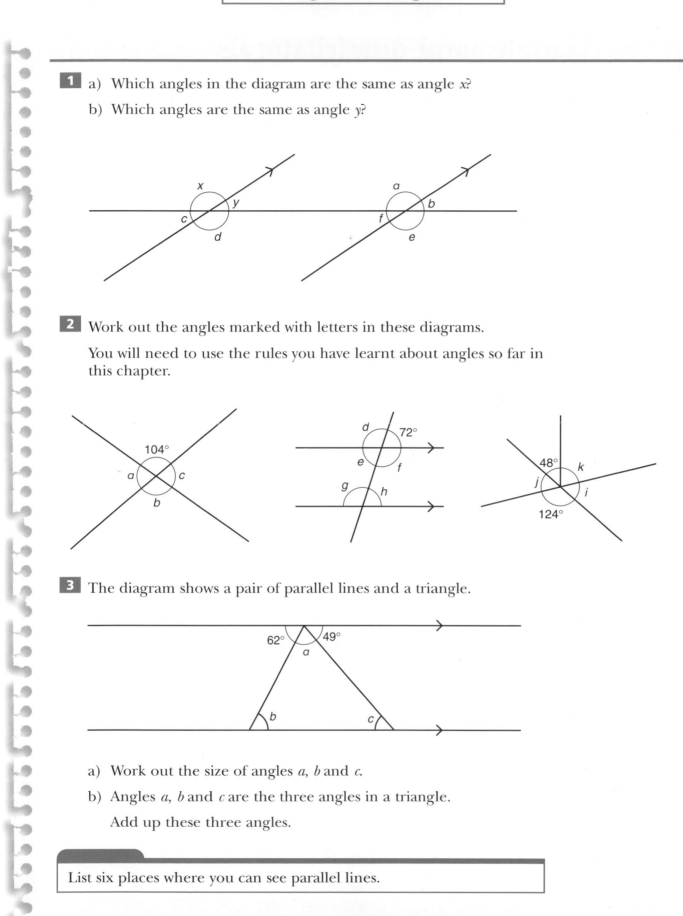

2 Work out the angles marked with letters in these diagrams.

You will need to use the rules you have learnt about angles so far in this chapter.

3 The diagram shows a pair of parallel lines and a triangle.

a) Work out the size of angles *a*, *b* and *c*.

b) Angles *a*, *b* and *c* are the three angles in a triangle.

Add up these three angles.

List six places where you can see parallel lines.

Triangles and quadrilaterals

A **triangle** is any three-sided shape.

Measure each of the angles in the triangles below.

Add up the three angles for each triangle.

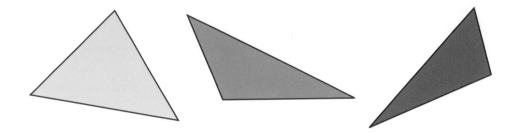

Angles in a triangle add up to 180°.

A **quadrilateral** is any four-sided shape.

Any quadrilateral can be split up into two triangles by drawing in a diagonal, like this:

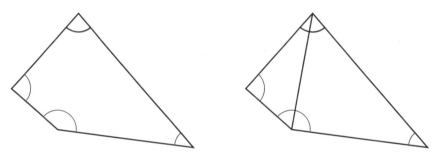

The angles in the quadrilateral must add up to the same as the angles in the two triangles.

So the angles in any quadrilateral must add up to 2 × 180° = 360°.

Angles in a quadrilateral add up to 360°.

A rectangle is a kind of quadrilateral.

It has four right angles.

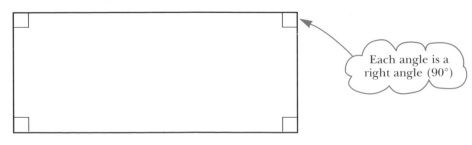

Each angle is a right angle (90°)

 What do 4 right angles add up to?

1 Find the angles marked with letters in these triangles and quadrilaterals.

They are not drawn accurately so you will need the rules on the opposite page.

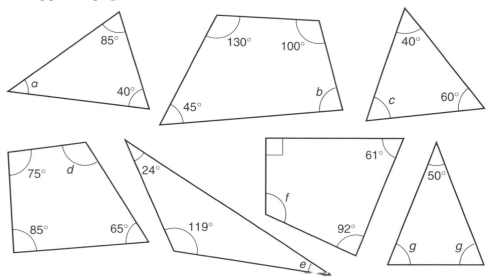

2 Find the angles marked with letters in the diagrams below.

You will need to use the rules about angles that you have learnt so far in this chapter.

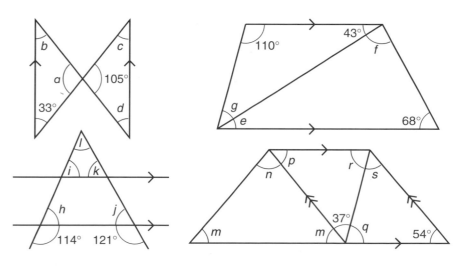

Road signs are made in a number of shapes.

What do the different shapes tell you?

Give some examples.

Interior angles of polygons

A **polygon** is a shape with several sides.

The angles inside a polygon are called the **interior angles**

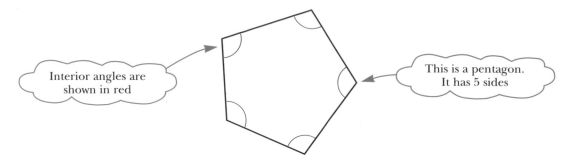

Interior angles are shown in red

This is a pentagon. It has 5 sides

A quick way of working out the sum of the interior angles of any polygon is by splitting it into triangles. The pentagon can be split into 3 triangles.

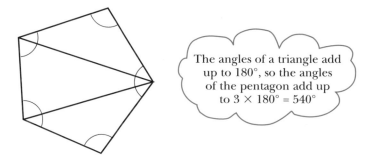

The angles of a triangle add up to 180°, so the angles of the pentagon add up to 3 × 180° = 540°

 Try splitting some other polygons into triangles. What is the rule for the number of triangles you can make?

Another way of finding the sum of the interior angles is to use the formula

Angle sum of a polygon = (Number of sides − 2) × 180°

 Why do you think this formula works?

A polygon is **regular** if all its sides are the same length and all its angles are equal. You can find the size of each interior angle by dividing the angle sum by the number of sides.

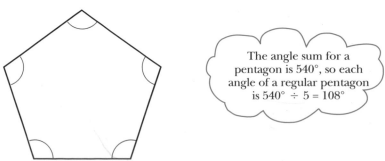

The angle sum for a pentagon is 540°, so each angle of a regular pentagon is 540° ÷ 5 = 108°

1

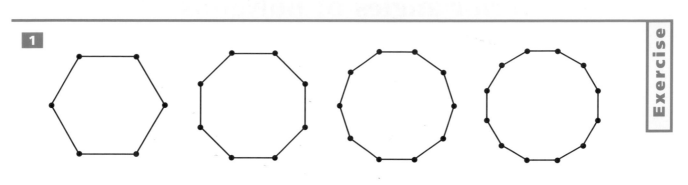

a) Copy and split each polygon into triangles.

b) Work out the angle sum of each polygon by multiplying the number of triangles by 180°.

c) Use the formula on the opposite page to work out the angle sum for each polygon. Check you get the same answers as in b).

2 Work out the interior angle of

a) a regular hexagon

b) a regular octagon

c) a regular decagon (10 sides)

d) a regular dodecagon (12 sides).

3 Here is a regular pentagon which has been split into 5 congruent (equal) triangles.

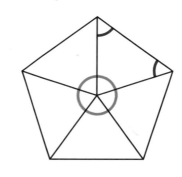

a) Work out the size of each blue angle.

b) Use your answer to a) to work out the size of each red angle.

c) Use your answer to b) to work out the interior angle of the pentagon.

4 Repeat question 3 for this regular hexagon:

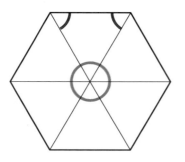

Stars are often used for decoration. The diagram shows how you can use a regular pentagon to make a 5-pointed star. Make one for yourself out of cardboard.

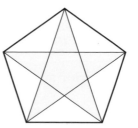

Now use a regular hexagon to make a 6-pointed star and a regular octagon to make an 8-pointed star.

Exterior angles of polygons

Sue is using a robot to draw a regular octagon.

She needs to know what angle the robot has to turn through each time.

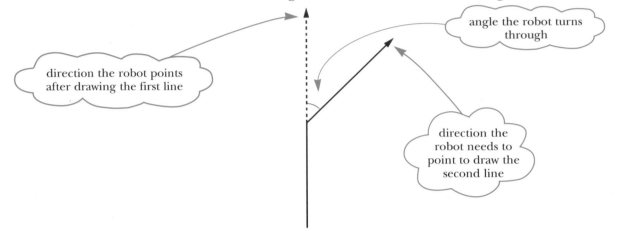

direction the robot points after drawing the first line

angle the robot turns through

direction the robot needs to point to draw the second line

This diagram shows all the angles the robot has to turn through.

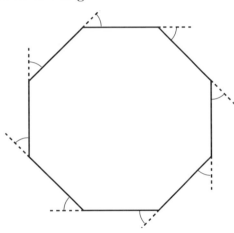

Sue could use LOGO instead of the robot

These are called the **exterior angles** of the octagon.

When it draws the octagon, the robot makes one complete turn. So it turns through 360° altogether.

What instructions should Sue give to the robot?

Sue works out that there are 8 angles, so each exterior angle must be 360° ÷ 8 = 45°.

> **Exterior angle of a regular polygon = 360° ÷ Number of sides**

What happens if the robot turns too much each time?

What happens if it turns too little each time?

1 Use the rule on the opposite page to work out the exterior angle of each of these polygons.

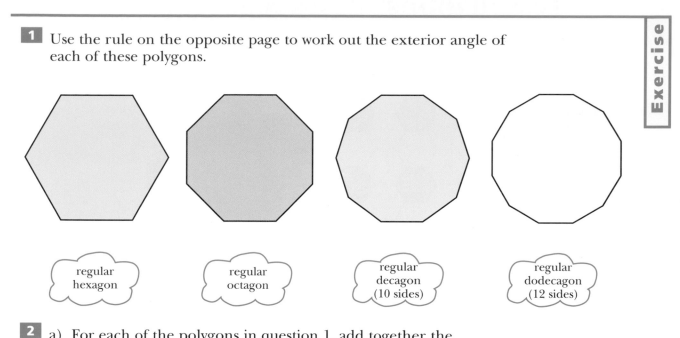

regular hexagon

regular octagon

regular decagon (10 sides)

regular dodecagon (12 sides)

2 a) For each of the polygons in question 1, add together the interior angle and the exterior angle.
(You worked out the interior angles in question 2 on page 45.)
What do you notice?

b) Explain why this happens.

3 a) Work out the exterior angle for each of these regular polygons.

(i) 9 sides

(ii) 25 sides

(iii) 100 sides.

b) Now work out the interior angle of each of them.
(You will need to use your answer to question 2b).)

The more sides a polygon has, the more it looks like a circle. So if you want to program a robot to draw a circle, you have to program it to draw a polygon with lots of sides.

Write a set of instructions for a robot (or LOGO) to draw a circle.

Tessellations

Look at these designs for floor tilings:

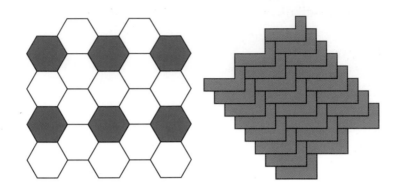

These patterns are examples of **tessellations**.

A tessellation is a repeating pattern without any gaps, made up of **congruent** shapes fitted together.

(Congruent means exactly the same size and shape.)

Tessellations can be made with very complicated shapes, as well as simple ones like those above. The Dutch artist M.C. Escher used fascinating tessellations in his work. Here are two examples:

'Reptiles'

'Day and Night'

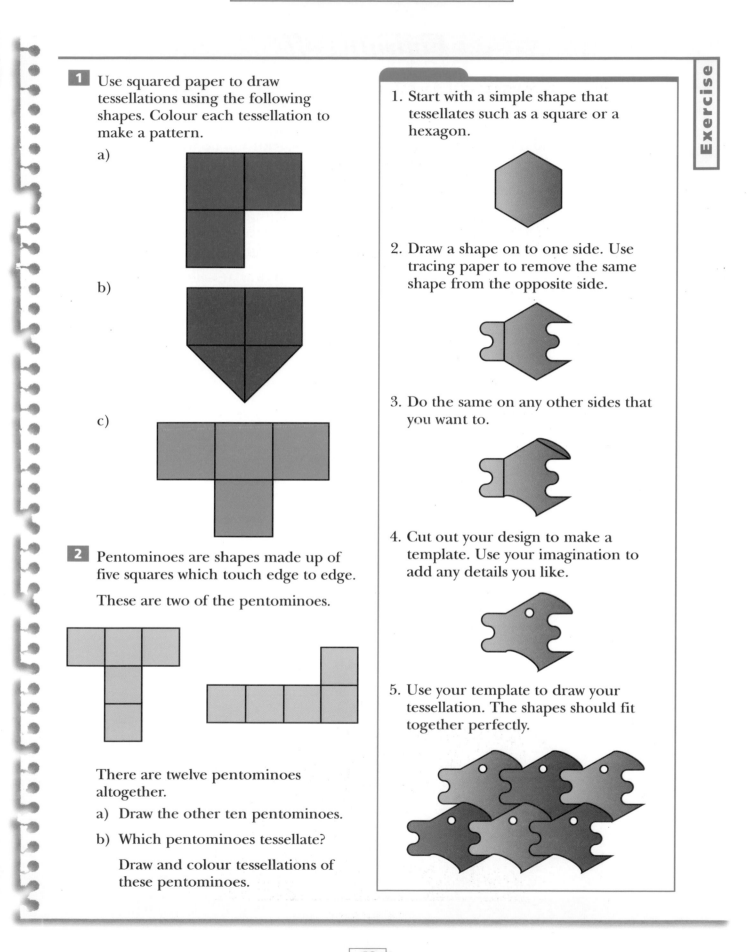

1 Use squared paper to draw tessellations using the following shapes. Colour each tessellation to make a pattern.

a)

b)

c)

2 Pentominoes are shapes made up of five squares which touch edge to edge.

These are two of the pentominoes.

There are twelve pentominoes altogether.

a) Draw the other ten pentominoes.

b) Which pentominoes tessellate?

Draw and colour tessellations of these pentominoes.

1. Start with a simple shape that tessellates such as a square or a hexagon.

2. Draw a shape on to one side. Use tracing paper to remove the same shape from the opposite side.

3. Do the same on any other sides that you want to.

4. Cut out your design to make a template. Use your imagination to add any details you like.

5. Use your template to draw your tessellation. The shapes should fit together perfectly.

Finishing off

Use the questions in the next exercise to check that you understand everything.

Mixed exercise

1 Find the angles marked with letters in the diagrams below.

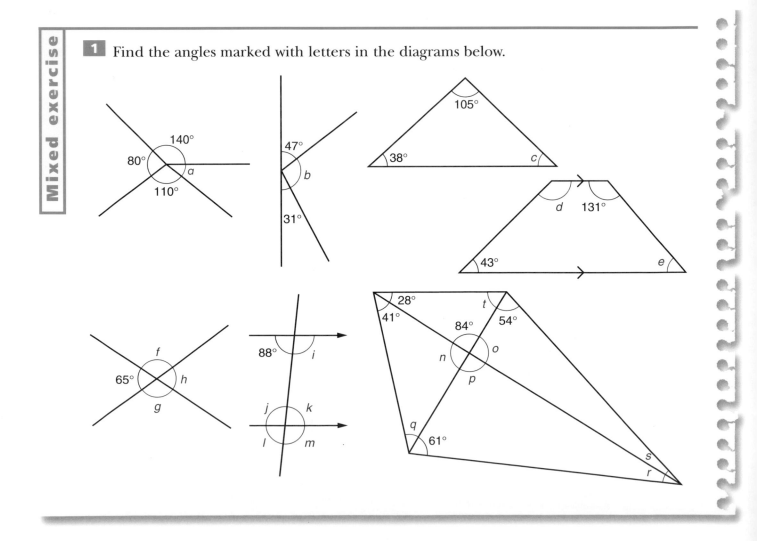

2 Find the sum of the interior angles of the polygon shown below.

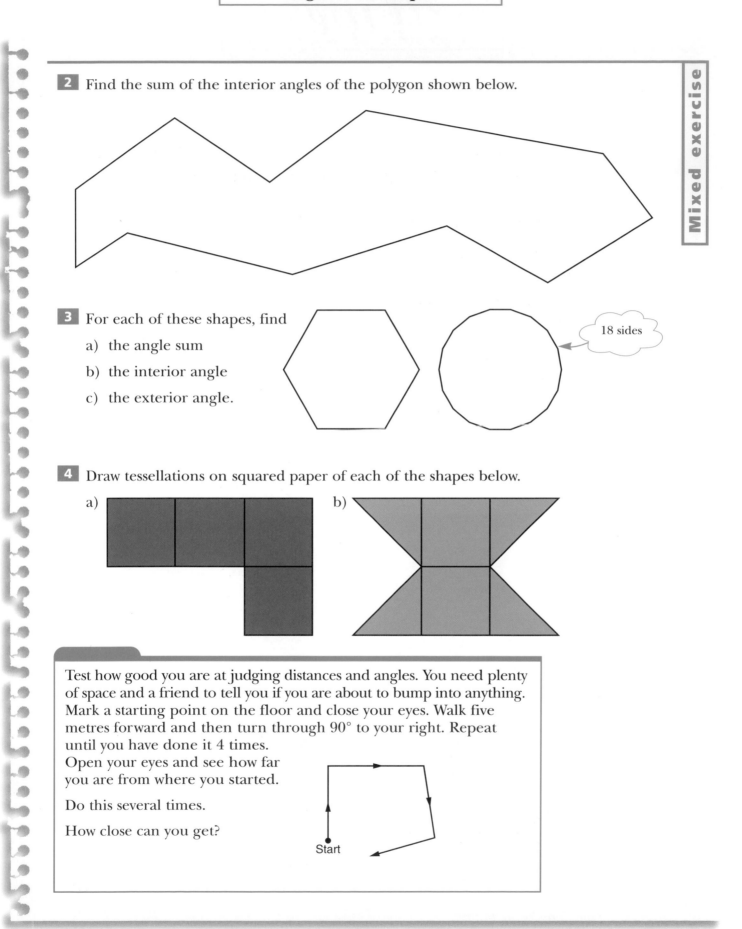

3 For each of these shapes, find

a) the angle sum

b) the interior angle

c) the exterior angle.

18 sides

4 Draw tessellations on squared paper of each of the shapes below.

a)

b)

Test how good you are at judging distances and angles. You need plenty of space and a friend to tell you if you are about to bump into anything. Mark a starting point on the floor and close your eyes. Walk five metres forward and then turn through 90° to your right. Repeat until you have done it 4 times.
Open your eyes and see how far you are from where you started.

Do this several times.

How close can you get?

Start

Five

Decimals

Before you start this chapter you should be able to

★ change $\frac{1}{4}$, $\frac{1}{2}$ and $\frac{3}{4}$ into decimals

★ change tenths and hundredths into decimals.

Tenths and hundredths

This number line is split into tenths.

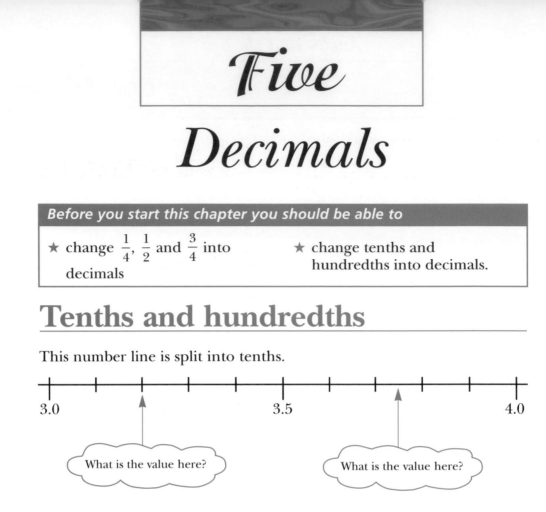

What is the value here?

What is the value here?

Adding and subtracting

This is the design of Sophie's garden:

She wants to know how long her lawn is.

She works it out like this:

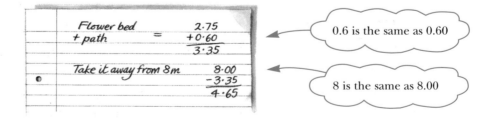

0.6 is the same as 0.60

8 is the same as 8.00

 How long is the lawn?

Decimals

1 Write down the tape measure readings.

a)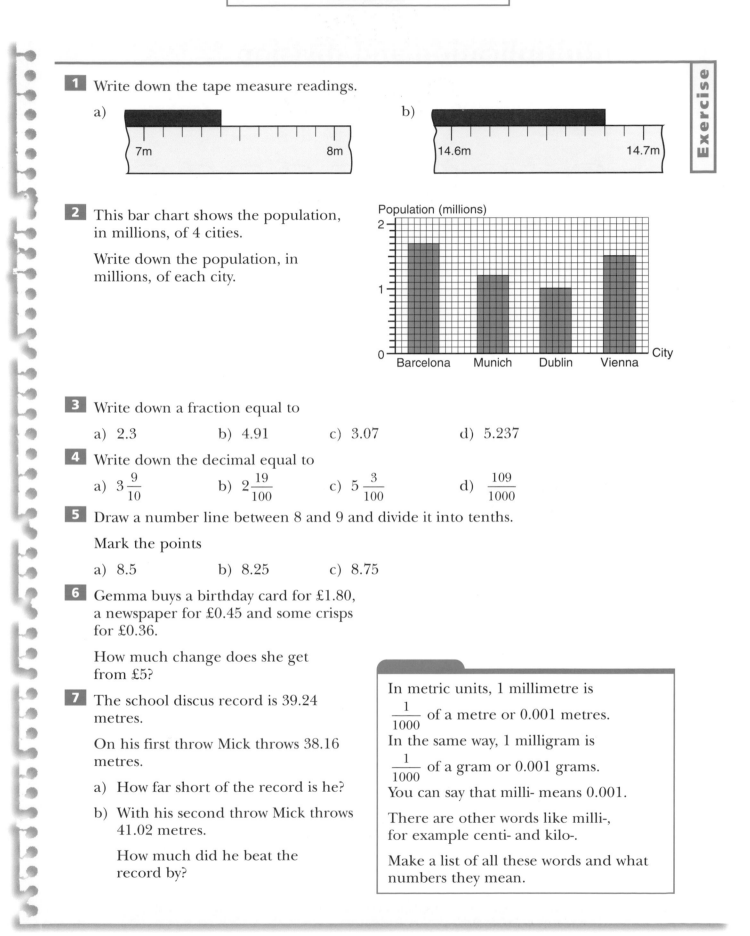

7m   8m

b)

14.6m   14.7m

2 This bar chart shows the population, in millions, of 4 cities.

Write down the population, in millions, of each city.

Population (millions)

2

1

0

Barcelona   Munich   Dublin   Vienna   City

3 Write down a fraction equal to

a) 2.3   b) 4.91   c) 3.07   d) 5.237

4 Write down the decimal equal to

a) $3\frac{9}{10}$ b) $2\frac{19}{100}$ c) $5\frac{3}{100}$ d) $\frac{109}{1000}$

5 Draw a number line between 8 and 9 and divide it into tenths.

Mark the points

a) 8.5   b) 8.25   c) 8.75

6 Gemma buys a birthday card for £1.80, a newspaper for £0.45 and some crisps for £0.36.

How much change does she get from £5?

7 The school discus record is 39.24 metres.

On his first throw Mick throws 38.16 metres.

a) How far short of the record is he?

b) With his second throw Mick throws 41.02 metres.

How much did he beat the record by?

In metric units, 1 millimetre is $\frac{1}{1000}$ of a metre or 0.001 metres.

In the same way, 1 milligram is $\frac{1}{1000}$ of a gram or 0.001 grams.

You can say that milli- means 0.001.

There are other words like milli-, for example centi- and kilo-.

Make a list of all these words and what numbers they mean.

Multiplication and division

Rachel works in a coffee shop.

She pours out 2.5 litres of lemonade for 10 children so that they all get the same.

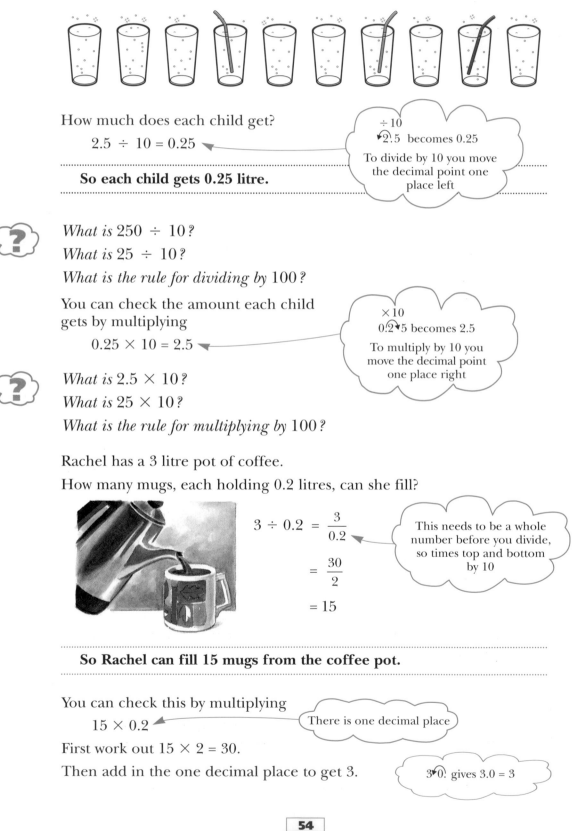

How much does each child get?

$$2.5 \div 10 = 0.25$$

> ÷ 10
> 2.5 becomes 0.25
>
> To divide by 10 you move the decimal point one place left

So each child gets 0.25 litre.

? *What is* $250 \div 10$?

What is $25 \div 10$?

What is the rule for dividing by 100?

You can check the amount each child gets by multiplying

$$0.25 \times 10 = 2.5$$

> × 10
> 0.25 becomes 2.5
>
> To multiply by 10 you move the decimal point one place right

? *What is* 2.5×10?

What is 25×10?

What is the rule for multiplying by 100?

Rachel has a 3 litre pot of coffee.

How many mugs, each holding 0.2 litres, can she fill?

$$3 \div 0.2 = \frac{3}{0.2}$$

$$= \frac{30}{2}$$

$$= 15$$

> This needs to be a whole number before you divide, so times top and bottom by 10

So Rachel can fill 15 mugs from the coffee pot.

You can check this by multiplying

$$15 \times 0.2$$

> There is one decimal place

First work out $15 \times 2 = 30$.

Then add in the one decimal place to get 3.

> 3.0. gives 3.0 = 3

Decimals

1 Work out

   a) 1.7×10 b) 1.7×100 c) 1.7×1000

   d) $3.2 \div 10$ e) $3.2 \div 100$ f) $3.2 \div 1000$

2 Work out

   a) 2×1.5 b) 4×0.2 c) 3×5.4 d) 2.6×1.2

3 Work out

   a) $4 \div 0.8$ b) $3.2 \div 0.4$ c) $3.9 \div 0.6$ d) $5 \div 0.25$

4 Caroline buys 10 metres of garden fencing at £3.25 per metre.

   a) How much does she pay?

   b) How much do 100 metres cost?

5 A pen costs £0.18.

How much do 100 pens cost?

6 The temperature in Blackpool is 30 °C.

   a) Multiply 30 by 1.8 and then add 32 to get the temperature in °F.

It is 20 °C in Scarborough.

   b) What is this in °F? (You need to do the same thing: multiply 20 by 1.8 and then add 32.)

7 Rory buys 10 oranges, 0.6 kg of green peppers, 0.75 kg of mushrooms. How much change does he get from £10?

8 It costs £120 to hire a boat.
The cost is shared between 10 people.

How much does each person pay?

9 Alex is 150 cm tall.   (100 cm = 1 m)

   a) Divide this by 100 to get her height in metres.

   b) Julie is 1.65 m tall.

Multiply this by 100 to get her height in cm.

Find out the prices of three magazines that interest you.

How much do you save by taking out an annual subscription?

Why do companies offer annual subscriptions at a cheaper rate?

Fractions to decimals

You know that $\frac{1}{4} = 0.25$, $\frac{1}{2} = 0.5$ and $\frac{3}{4} = 0.75$.

What about $\frac{1}{8}$?

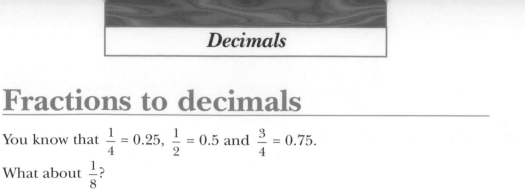

$\frac{1}{8}$ is half of $\frac{1}{4}$

What decimal is half of 0.25?

$$0.25 \div 2 = 0.125$$

So $\frac{1}{8} = \textbf{0.125}$

Also, $\frac{1}{8}$ is $1 \div 8 = 0.125$

$\begin{array}{r} 0.125 \\ 8\overline{)1.000} \end{array}$

So again, $\frac{1}{8} = 0.125$.

We can do this to change any fraction into a decimal.

 *What is $\frac{1}{5}$ as a decimal?*

Something interesting happens when we work out $\frac{1}{3}$ as a decimal.

$$\frac{1}{3} = 1 \div 3 = 0.333\ldots$$

the 3s go on forever!

$\begin{array}{r} 0.333\ldots \\ 3\overline{)1.000\ldots} \end{array}$

'0.3 recurring'

This is a **recurring decimal**.

Instead of writing out all the 3s (that would take forever!) we write $0.\dot{3}$.

The same thing happens for $\frac{1}{6}$.

$$\frac{1}{6} = 1 \div 6 = 0.166\ldots$$

$\begin{array}{r} 0.166\ldots \\ 6\overline{)1.000\ldots} \end{array}$

So $\frac{1}{6} = \textbf{0.16}\dot{}$

'0.16 recurring'

1 Change the fraction to a decimal:

a) $\dfrac{3}{5}$　　　　b) $\dfrac{3}{8}$　　　　c) $\dfrac{9}{20}$　　　　d) $\dfrac{5}{4}$

e) $\dfrac{8}{25}$　　　　f) $\dfrac{1}{16}$　　　　g) $\dfrac{7}{2}$　　　　h) $\dfrac{13}{5}$

2 Change the fraction to a recurring decimal:

a) $\dfrac{4}{3}$　　　　b) $\dfrac{1}{9}$　　　　c) $\dfrac{7}{6}$　　　　d) $\dfrac{4}{9}$

Investigation

What is $\dfrac{1}{11}$ as a decimal?

Work out $1 \div 11$.

$$\begin{array}{r} 0.0909... \\ 11)\overline{1.0000...} \end{array}$$

So $\dfrac{1}{11} = 0.0909...$

a) In the same way, find the decimal form of

(i) $\dfrac{2}{11}$　　　　(ii) $\dfrac{6}{11}$.

These results have been put into this table.

Fraction	Decimal
$\dfrac{1}{11}$	0.0909...
$\dfrac{2}{11}$	0.1818...
$\dfrac{3}{11}$	
$\dfrac{4}{11}$	
$\dfrac{5}{11}$	
$\dfrac{6}{11}$	0.5454...
$\dfrac{7}{11}$	
$\dfrac{8}{11}$	
$\dfrac{9}{11}$	
$\dfrac{10}{11}$	

b) What do you think the missing decimals are?

Find out which temperatures are whole numbers of degrees in both Celsius and Fahrenheit.

What temperature is the same number of degrees on both scales?

Finishing off

Now that you have finished this chapter you should be able to

★ change between decimal form and fractions

★ add and subtract decimals

★ multiply decimals (including multiplying by 10, 100, etc.)

★ divide decimals (including dividing by 10, 100, etc.)

★ work out squares and square roots of decimals.

Use the questions in the next exercise to check that you understand everything.

Mixed exercise

1 How tall are these people?

a)

b)

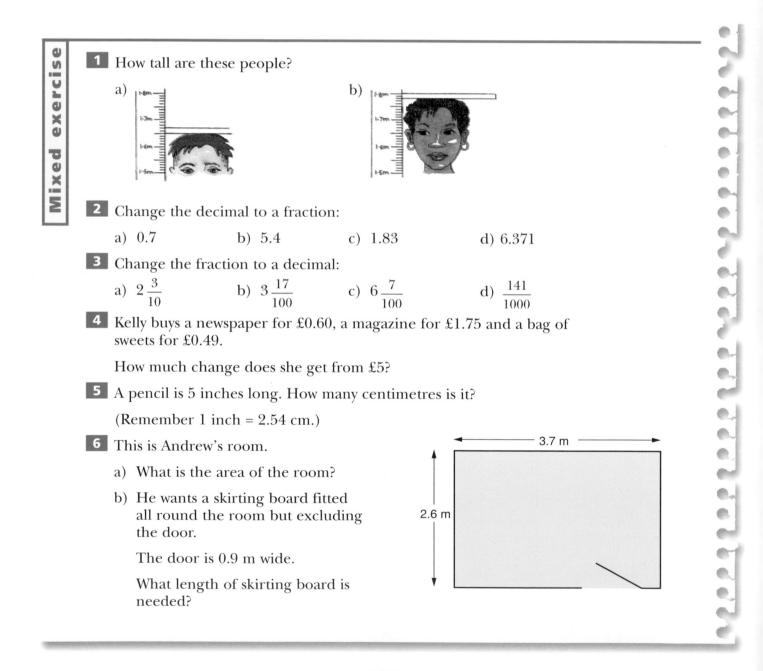

2 Change the decimal to a fraction:

a) 0.7   b) 5.4   c) 1.83   d) 6.371

3 Change the fraction to a decimal:

a) $2\frac{3}{10}$ b) $3\frac{17}{100}$ c) $6\frac{7}{100}$ d) $\frac{141}{1000}$

4 Kelly buys a newspaper for £0.60, a magazine for £1.75 and a bag of sweets for £0.49.

How much change does she get from £5?

5 A pencil is 5 inches long. How many centimetres is it?

(Remember 1 inch = 2.54 cm.)

6 This is Andrew's room.

a) What is the area of the room?

b) He wants a skirting board fitted all round the room but excluding the door.

The door is 0.9 m wide.

What length of skirting board is needed?

3.7 m

2.6 m

7 Ceri buys 10 tins of cat food.

a) How much does she pay?

The supermarket pays £500 for 1000 tins of the cat food.

b) How much do they pay for 1 tin?

8 Laura buys 0.5 kg of grapes, 1.2 kg of tomatoes and 3 peaches. How much change does she get from £10?

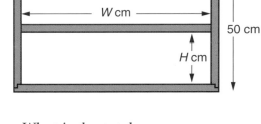

9 A path is 9 metres long. How many paving slabs are needed to make the path if each slab is

a) 0.9 metres long?   b) 0.6 metres long?

10 This is Shamir's bookcase. The wood is 1.6 cm thick.

a) Work out the inside width, W cm, of the shelves.

b) The shelves are of equal height.

Work out the inside height, H cm, of each shelf.

11 Dale buys twenty litres of petrol at £0.64 per litre. What is the total cost?

12 50 000 people each pay £30 to attend a pop concert.

a) How much money is collected?

b) 4000 T-shirts are sold at the concert. They cost £52 000 altogether.

How much does one T-shirt cost?

13 Find the value of

a) 5.3^2 b) $\sqrt{8.41}$

c) 6.8^2 d) $\sqrt{15.21}$

14 Change these fractions into decimals.

a) $\frac{4}{5}$ b) $\frac{5}{8}$

c) $\frac{7}{20}$ d) $\frac{5}{6}$

15 Arrange these in order of size.

Start with the smallest.

    5.1, 5, 5.02, 5.01

Find examples of measuring instruments with scales in

a) whole   b) 0.5

c) 0.2   d) 0.1   units.

Can you find examples of any other divisions?

Six

Sequences

Before you start this chapter you should

★ understand the word formula ★ know that letters can be used to stand for numbers.

Patterns

Look at this pattern.

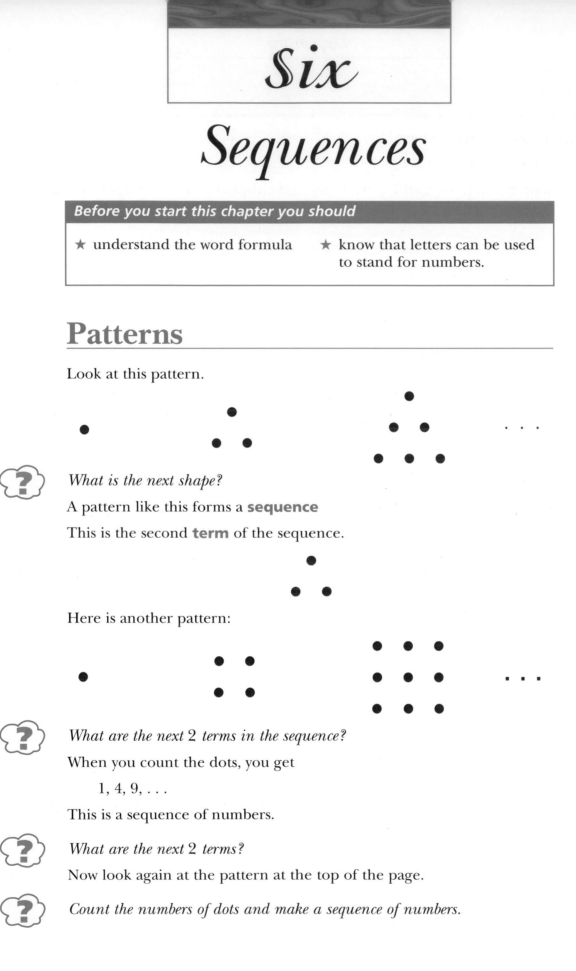

What is the next shape?

A pattern like this forms a **sequence**

This is the second **term** of the sequence.

Here is another pattern:

What are the next 2 terms in the sequence?

When you count the dots, you get

1, 4, 9, . . .

This is a sequence of numbers.

What are the next 2 terms?

Now look again at the pattern at the top of the page.

Count the numbers of dots and make a sequence of numbers.

1 Write down the next 3 terms in each of these sequences.

a) 2, 4, 6, . . .   b) 5, 10, 15, . . .   c) 1, 3, 5, . . .

2 a) Draw the next 3 shapes in this sequence.

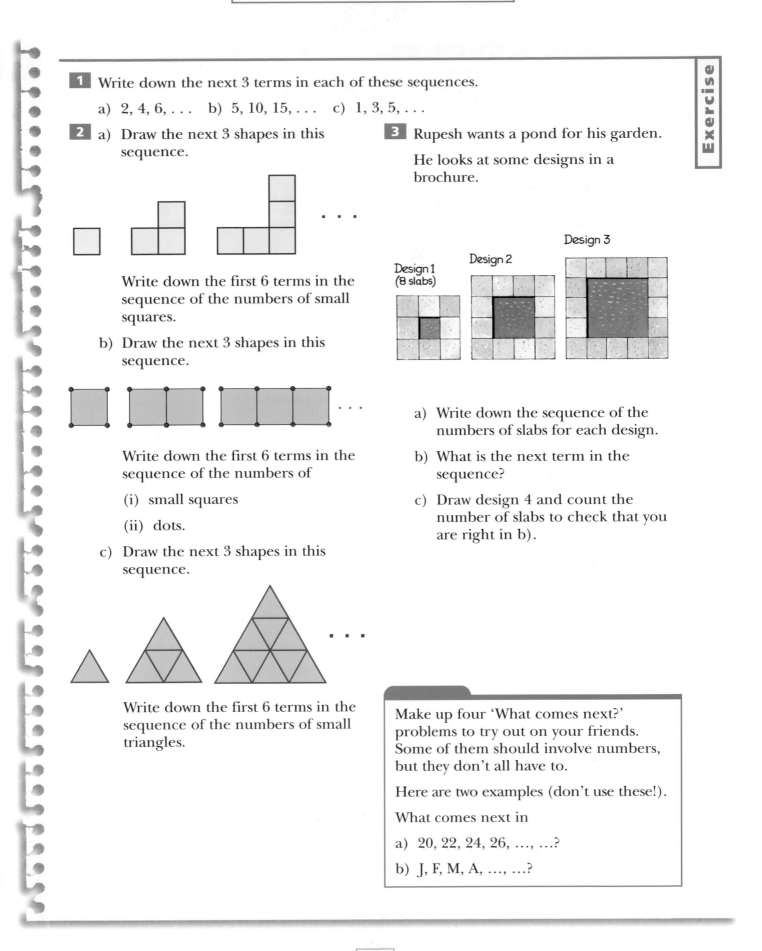

Write down the first 6 terms in the sequence of the numbers of small squares.

b) Draw the next 3 shapes in this sequence.

Write down the first 6 terms in the sequence of the numbers of

(i) small squares

(ii) dots.

c) Draw the next 3 shapes in this sequence.

Write down the first 6 terms in the sequence of the numbers of small triangles.

3 Rupesh wants a pond for his garden.

He looks at some designs in a brochure.

Design 1 (8 slabs)   Design 2   Design 3

a) Write down the sequence of the numbers of slabs for each design.

b) What is the next term in the sequence?

c) Draw design 4 and count the number of slabs to check that you are right in b).

Make up four 'What comes next?' problems to try out on your friends. Some of them should involve numbers, but they don't all have to.

Here are two examples (don't use these!).

What comes next in

a) 20, 22, 24, 26, ..., ...?

b) J, F, M, A, ..., ...?

More sequences

During the day, trams go from Altrincham to Manchester every 12 minutes.

Trams leave Altrincham at this many minutes past every hour:

   0, 12, 24, 36 . . .

This means o'clock

This means 12 minutes past, etc.

The connection between the times is

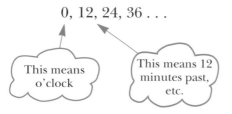

   +12   +12   +12   +12

   0 → 12 → 24 → 36

The rule is ADD 12 MINUTES.

 What happens to this sequence when it gets to 60?

Now look at this sequence:

   20, 18, 16, 14, . . .

 What are the next 3 terms?

The connection between successive terms is

   −2   −2   −2

   20 → 18 → 16 → 14

So the rule is SUBTRACT 2 and the sequence carries on like this:

   20, 18, 16, 14, 12, 10, . . .

1 Write down the next three terms of each sequence.

Write down the rule that you use.

a) 2, 4, 6, 8, . . .

b) 1, 5, 9, 13, . . .

c) 10, 9, 8, 7, . . .

d) 128, 120, 112, 104, . . .

e) 0.5, 1, 1.5, 2, . . .

f) 9, 7, 5, 3, . . .

2 Anna lives in a tower block.

The lift has broken down again.

She counts the steps and calls out the number as she reaches each floor.

The sequence of numbers is

15, 30, 45, . . .

a) What number does she call out next?

b) How many steps are there between each floor?

c) Anna lives on the 7th floor. How many steps does she have to climb?

3 Ella is walking down the street.

a) She sees these house-number signs on the right.

EVENS	EVENS	EVENS
2 – 8	10 – 16	18 – 24

What are the next 3 signs in this sequence?

b) She sees these house-number signs on the left.

ODDS	ODDS	ODDS
1 – 15	17 – 31	33 – 47

What are the next 3 signs in this sequence?

c) Ella is visiting house number 71. Which sign is she looking for?

4 John has 4 hospital appointments, one every two weeks beginning on 4 September.

Write down the sequence of dates for John's appointments.

SEPTEMBER

1
2
3
4   *Hospital .*
5
6

5 The Olympic Games are held every four years.

They were held in 1996.

Write down the years of the next three Olympic Games after this date.

Mandy and Phil always have a house party on the first Sunday of the year. In 2001, this is on 7 January.

Write down the sequence of dates of the party for the following 10 years.

Finding *n*

At a farm show, Mr Brown makes sheep pens with fences like this.

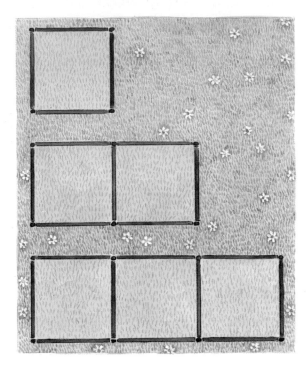

4 fences make 1 pen

7 fences make 2 pens

10 fences make 3 pens

 How many fences does he need to make 4 pens?

Look at the number of fences for each pen.

Number of pens	Number of fences
1 ⟶	4
2 ⟶	7
3 ⟶	10

To find the number of fences, you multiply the number of pens by 3 and then add 1.

Number of fences = (Number of pens × 3) + 1

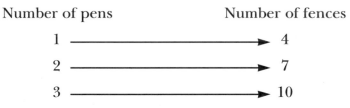

Call this *n*   Call this *p*

We can write it like this:

$n = (p \times 3) + 1$

If we want 4 pens, $p = 4$ so $n = (4 \times 3) + 1 = 13$.

1 Look at this sequence:

1, 6, 11, 16, . . .

The arrow diagram looks like this:

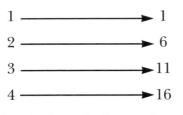

term number	term
1 ⟶	1
2 ⟶	6
3 ⟶	11
4 ⟶	16

a) What is the rule for getting the next term?

b) What is term number 5?

2 Look at this sequence:

60, 55, 50, 45, . . .

Copy and complete this arrow diagram:

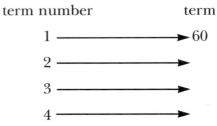

term number	term
1 ⟶	60
2 ⟶	
3 ⟶	
4 ⟶	

a) What is the rule for getting the next term?

b) What term number is 25?

3 Michelle is given £50 for her birthday.

Each week after her birthday, she gets £10 pocket money.

She is saving up for a mountain bike, which costs £130.

a) Write down a sequence showing how much she has after 1 week, 2 weeks, etc.

b) How much does she have after 5 weeks?

c) Draw an arrow diagram to show how much she has saved each week.

Weeks after birthday, N	Amount saved, £A
1 ⟶	£60
2 ⟶	

d) Work out a formula in words and letters for the amount Michelle saves after N weeks.

e) How long does it take her to get the bike?

The diagram shows a house of cards with three layers. If you are careful you can build card houses with more layers. Find the numbers of cards in each layer as a sequence and find a formula for it.

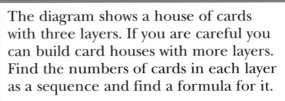

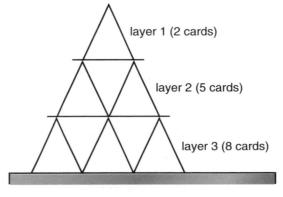

layer 1 (2 cards)

layer 2 (5 cards)

layer 3 (8 cards)

More number sequences

Vicky is a scientist.

The number of bacteria in her experiment doubles every week.

At the start there are 2.

After 1 week there are 4.

After 2 weeks there are 8.

 How many bacteria are there after 3 weeks?

The numbers make this sequence:

   2, 4, 8, 16, . . .

The connection between them is

   ×2   ×2   ×2   ×2
   2 → 4 → 8 → 16

So the rule is MULTIPLY BY 2.

The Men's Singles Competition at Wimbledon has 128 players in round 1.

Half of the players (those who lose their matches) are knocked out at every round.

There are 64 players in round 2.

There are 32 players in round 3.

 How many are there in round 4?

The numbers make this sequence:

   128, 64, 32, 16, . . .

The connection between them is

   ÷2   ÷2   ÷2   ÷2
   128   64   32   16

So the rule is DIVIDE BY 2.

 How many rounds before there is a winner?

Sequences

1 Write down the next 3 terms for each sequence.

Write down the rule that you use.

a) 1, 2, 4, . . .

b) 5, 10, 20, . . .

c) 1, 3, 9, . . .

d) 10, 100, 1000, . . .

2 Write down the next 3 terms for each sequence.

Write down the rule that you use.

a) 800, 400, 200, . . .

b) 100 000, 10 000, 1000, . . .

c) 64, 32, 16, . . .

3 Jane is folding a large sheet of thin card, 1 metre by 1 metre.

The card is 1 mm thick.

She folds it in half.

Now the card is 2 mm thick.

She folds the card in half again.

a) How thick is it now?

Jane carries on folding the card in half like this.

b) Write down the first 6 terms in the sequence of how thick the card is, starting with 1 mm.

Before she folds it, the area of the card is 1 m^2.

c) Write down the first 6 terms in the sequence of the area of the folded card, starting with 1 m^2.

d) What is the area of the card when it is 8 mm thick?

4 Usma plants a creeper plant. It grows along her fence.

After 1 year it covers 1 fence panel.

Usma knows that this type of plant doubles every year.

a) How many panels does the plant cover after 2 years?

b) How many panels does it cover after 3 years?

c) Usma has 16 panels on her fence altogether.

How long is it before the plant covers the whole fence?

Paper comes in various sizes.

The sizes, starting large and getting smaller, are called

A0, A1, A2, A3, A4, A5, . . .

Find out how the paper sizes in the sequence are related.

Finishing off

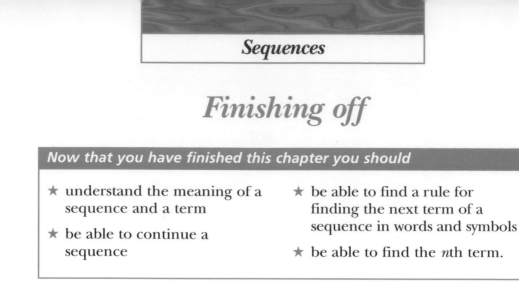

Now that you have finished this chapter you should

★ understand the meaning of a sequence and a term

★ be able to continue a sequence

★ be able to find a rule for finding the next term of a sequence in words and symbols

★ be able to find the *n*th term.

Use the questions in the next exercise to check that you understand everything.

Mixed exercise

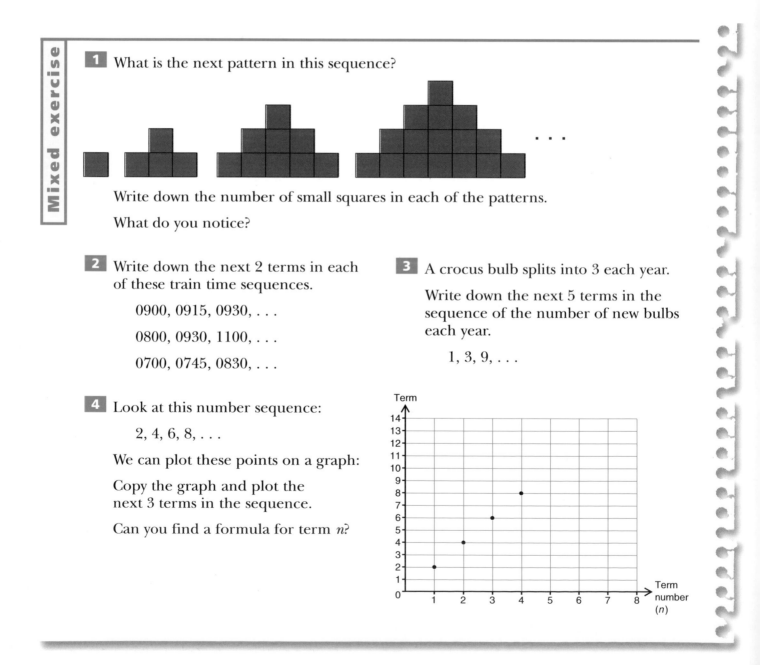

1 What is the next pattern in this sequence?

Write down the number of small squares in each of the patterns.

What do you notice?

2 Write down the next 2 terms in each of these train time sequences.

0900, 0915, 0930, . . .

0800, 0930, 1100, . . .

0700, 0745, 0830, . . .

3 A crocus bulb splits into 3 each year.

Write down the next 5 terms in the sequence of the number of new bulbs each year.

1, 3, 9, . . .

4 Look at this number sequence:

2, 4, 6, 8, . . .

We can plot these points on a graph:

Copy the graph and plot the next 3 terms in the sequence.

Can you find a formula for term *n*?

5 A small booklet is made by folding a sheet of A4 paper in half.

a) Now another sheet is folded and the two sheets are stapled like this:

How many pages does this booklet have?

b) Write down a sequence of the number of pages in a booklet made in this way.

c) Copy and complete the arrow diagram.

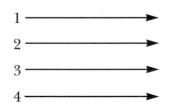

Number of   Number of pages
A4 sheets   in booklet

1 ——————————→

2 ——————————→

3 ——————————→

4 ——————————→

d) Copy and complete this sentence:

For each extra A4 sheet used the booklet has_____ more pages.

e) Find a formula for working out the number of pages in a booklet made with n A4 sheets.

In the activity on page 45 you made some stars.

In this activity you look at the angles of the points of the stars. You will find it helpful to draw the polygons in circles.

Here is a 9-sided polygon.

The angles at the centre are
$$360° \div 9 = 40°$$

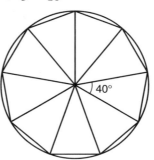

Draw stars with 5, 7, 9, … points and measure the angles. Find a formula connecting the angle, 180° and the number of points.

Do the same for stars with 6, 8, 10, … points.

Which stars do you think look best?

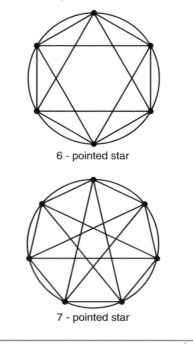

6 - pointed star

7 - pointed star

Seven

Percentages

Before you start this chapter you should

★ know the fraction and decimal equivalents of 50%, 25% and 75%

★ be able to calculate the percentage of a number.

Percentages, decimals and fractions

Ali is doing a survey for a travel agent.

He asks 50 people

Have you ever been to France?

20 people say 'yes'.

What is $\dfrac{20}{50}$ as a percentage and a decimal?

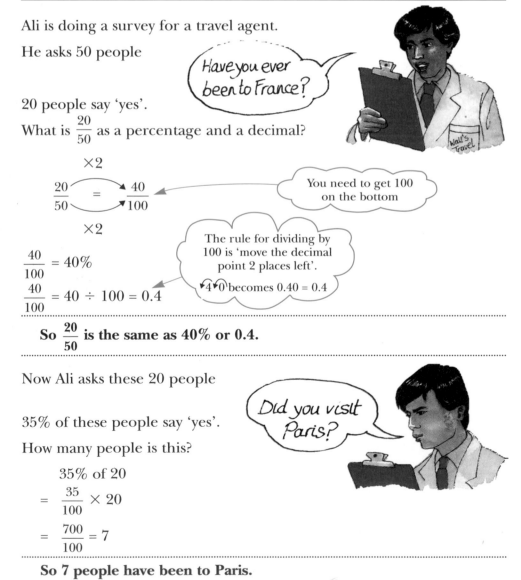

$$\overset{\times 2}{\underset{\times 2}{\dfrac{20}{50}}} = \dfrac{40}{100}$$

You need to get 100 on the bottom

$$\dfrac{40}{100} = 40\%$$

$$\dfrac{40}{100} = 40 \div 100 = 0.4$$

The rule for dividing by 100 is 'move the decimal point 2 places left'.

40 becomes 0.40 = 0.4

So $\dfrac{20}{50}$ is the same as 40% or 0.4.

Now Ali asks these 20 people

Did you visit Paris?

35% of these people say 'yes'.

How many people is this?

$$35\% \text{ of } 20$$

$$= \dfrac{35}{100} \times 20$$

$$= \dfrac{700}{100} = 7$$

So 7 people have been to Paris.

1 Look at this pie chart.

It shows the amount of sales a company makes in different parts of the world.

a) Which of these is the correct answer?

(i) The amount of sales in the UK is

A less than 25%   B 25%   C more than 25%

(ii) The amount of sales in the Rest of Europe is

A less than 50%   B 50%   C more than 50%

(iii) The amount of sales in the USA is

A less than 25%   B 25%   C more than 25%

b) Estimate the percentage of sales in other countries.

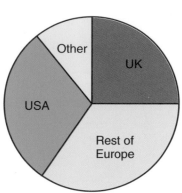

2 A survey asks a group of teenagers what time they went to bed last night.

This pie chart shows the results.

What percentage went to bed

a) before 10 p.m.?

b) after 10 p.m. but before midnight?

c) after midnight?

3 Each of these floor designs is made of 100 tiles.

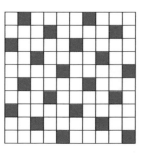 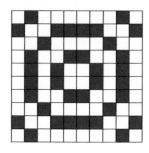

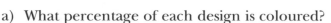

a) What percentage of each design is coloured?

b) Write each percentage as a fraction in its simplest form.

c) Write each percentage as a decimal.

Make two floor designs of your own where 20% of the tiles are white and the rest are black.

Look at real floors and tiles for ideas.

Percentage calculations

Stephen runs a fashion business.

Last year he made a profit of £150 000.

This year he makes 20% more profit.

He works out his total profit for this year like this:

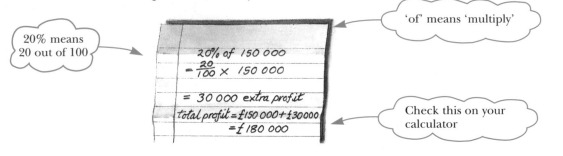

20% means 20 out of 100

'of' means 'multiply'

$$20\% \text{ of } 150\,000$$
$$= \frac{20}{100} \times 150\,000$$
$$= 30\,000 \text{ extra profit}$$
$$\text{total profit} = £150\,000 + £30\,000$$
$$= £180\,000$$

Check this on your calculator

So Stephen's total profit this year is £180 000.

Mark works for Stephen.

He earns £170 a week.

He gets a 3% pay rise.

Mark works out how much extra money he will get like this:

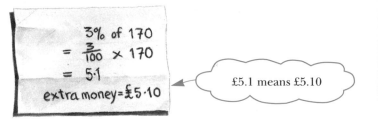

$$3\% \text{ of } 170$$
$$= \frac{3}{100} \times 170$$
$$= 5.1$$
$$\text{extra money} = £5.10$$

£5.1 means £5.10

 How much does Mark earn after the pay rise?

Staff get 15% discount when they buy clothes from Stephen.

Mark buys these clothes, worth £125.60.

£25 £45 £15·60 £40

His discount is 15% of £125.60.

He works it out like this:

$$15\% \text{ of } 125.60$$
$$= \frac{15}{100} \times 125.60$$
$$= 18.84$$
$$\text{discount} = £18.84$$

 How much does he pay for the clothes?

How much discount does he get off the polo-neck jumper?

1 Work out

a) 25% of 800   b) 80% of 300   c) 60% of 250   d) 50% of 133

e) 12% of 460   f) 75% of 1500   g) 40% of 320   h) 35% of 650

2 These flights are on special offer.

a) How much do you save if you book a flight to San Francisco today?

b) How much do you save if you book a flight to Tokyo today?

c) How much do you pay if you book a flight to Mexico today?

San Francisco	£240
Egypt	£200
Tokyo	£500
Mexico	£320

Book today for 10% discount

SPECIAL OFFER

3 Neil is given a 5% pay rise. He earns £8000 before the rise.

a) How much does he earn after the rise?

b) Neil goes out for a meal to celebrate.

It comes to £30 and he leaves a 15% tip.

How much tip does he leave?

4 Danielle's heating bills are £900.

How much would she save with roof insulation?

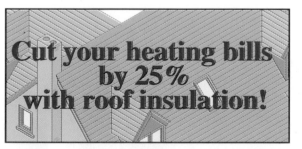

Cut your heating bills by 25% with roof insulation!

5 Sam sells her house for £60 000.

She pays the estate agent 1.75% of this.

a) How much does she pay the estate agent?

b) Sam buys carpets worth £1600 for her new house.

She pays cash and gets a 5% discount.

How much does she pay for the carpets?

Watch a television programme (with adverts) that is scheduled to take $\frac{1}{2}$ an hour.

What percentage of the time is adverts and what percentage is the programme itself?

Fractions to percentages

You know that $\frac{1}{4} = 25\%$, $\frac{1}{2} = 50\%$ and $\frac{3}{4} = 75\%$.

What about $\frac{3}{5}$?

One way to change $\frac{3}{5}$ into a percentage, is to work out an equivalent fraction with 100 on the bottom.

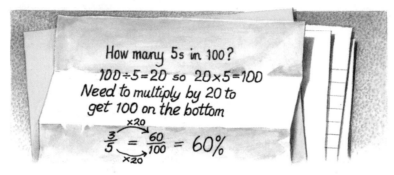

How many 5s in 100?
$100 \div 5 = 20$ so $20 \times 5 = 100$
Need to multiply by 20 to get 100 on the bottom

$\frac{3}{5} = \frac{60}{100} = 60\%$

Another way to do it is like this:

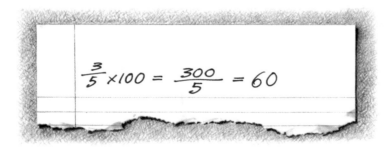

$\frac{3}{5} \times 100 = \frac{300}{5} = 60$

So $\frac{3}{5}$ is 60%.

What is $\frac{9}{20}$ as a percentage?

Work it out both ways to check you get the same answer.

What is $\frac{1}{8}$ as a percentage?

It is easier to use the second method for this.

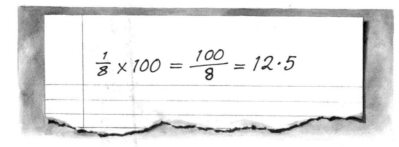

$\frac{1}{8} \times 100 = \frac{100}{8} = 12 \cdot 5$

So $\frac{1}{8}$ is 12.5%

Why is it easier to do it this way for $\frac{1}{8}$?

1 Change the fraction to a percentage:

a) $\dfrac{1}{5}$　　　　b) $\dfrac{7}{20}$　　　　c) $\dfrac{9}{25}$　　　　d) $\dfrac{3}{8}$

e) $\dfrac{39}{50}$　　　　f) $\dfrac{33}{40}$　　　　g) $\dfrac{68}{200}$　　　　h) $\dfrac{75}{120}$

2 In a survey of 40 teenagers (20 girls and 20 boys) 12 say they smoke.

a) What percentage of the teenagers smoke?

8 of the teenagers who smoke are girls, 4 are boys.

b) What percentage of the girls smoke?

c) What percentage of the boys smoke?

3 For each person, work out what percentage of their weekly wage is spent on housing.

a) Karen earns £80 a week and spends £40 a week on student accommodation.

b) Marie earns £180 a week and spends £60 a week on rent.

c) Jo earns £350 a week and spends £80 a week on her mortgage.

4 This table shows the profits of a CD shop over the four quarters of last year.

Quarter	Spring	Summer	Autumn	Winter
Profit (£)	21 000	34 000	38 000	27 000

a) What was the total profit last year?

b) What percentage of the total profit was made in summer?

c) What percentage of the total profit was made in autumn?

Look at the postmarks on the first class letters you receive during one week.

How many days does each letter take to arrive?

What percentage of the letters arrive the day after posting?

Proportions

Dr Lee is trying out 2 new migraine treatments.

She gives 50 patients treatment A and 50 patients treatment B.

Next day she asks the patients how they feel.

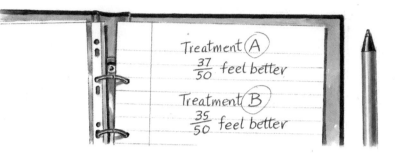

What percentage feel better after treatment A?

$$\frac{37}{50} = \frac{74}{100} = 74\%$$

74% feel better after treatment A.

What percentage feel better after treatment B?

Which treatment works better?

Dr Parker is also trying out the new treatments.

He gets these results:

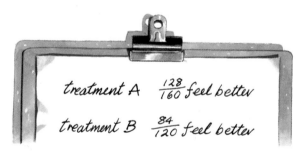

It's more difficult to work out which treatment works better for Dr Parker's patients.

He did not give the treatments to the same number of patients.

We can work out the **proportion** of patients who feel better.

With treatment A,

$\frac{128}{160} = 80\%$ or 0.8 feel better.

What percentage feel better with treatment B?

Which treatment works better for Dr Parker's patients?

1 Write each fraction as a decimal and as a percentage.

a) $\frac{3}{4}$　　b) $\frac{20}{80}$　　c) $\frac{17}{50}$　　d) $\frac{6}{10}$

e) $\frac{13}{15}$　　f) $\frac{6}{25}$　　g) $\frac{19}{20}$　　h) $\frac{7}{9}$

2 This table shows the members of two sports clubs.

	Female	Male
Tennis	24	17
Badminton	31	23

a) How many members are there in the tennis club?

b) What proportion of the tennis club are female?

c) Which club has a higher proportion of female members?

d) Which club has a higher proportion of male members?

3 Maureen manages a driving school.

She makes this table to compare her instructors.

Instructor	Number taking test	Number passing test
Arthur	45	26
Barry	53	17
Caroline	37	21

a) What proportion of Arthur's pupils pass the test?

b) What proportion of Barry's pupils pass the test?

c) What proportion of Caroline's pupils pass the test?

d) What do you think Maureen should do?

Ask 15 people you know to name the capital of Norway. (It's Oslo, if you have forgotten!)

What proportion get it right?

Finishing off

Use the questions in the next exercise to check that you understand everything.

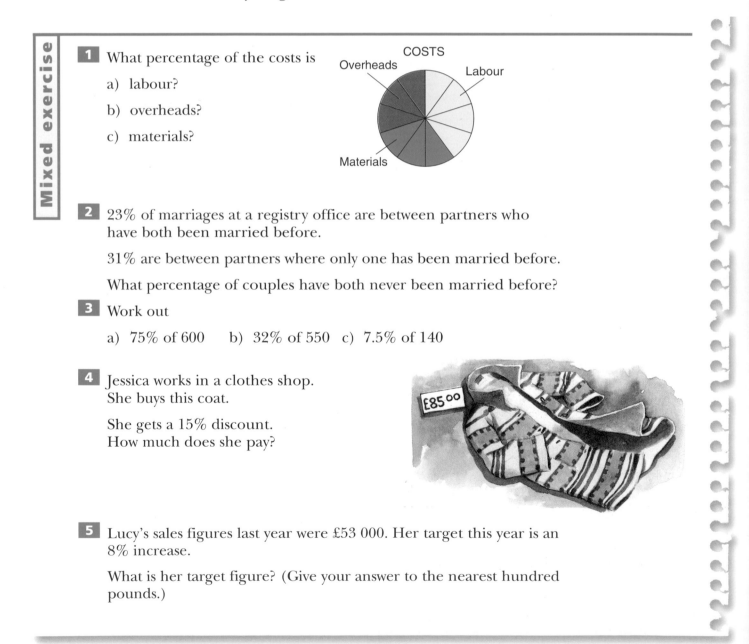

Mixed exercise

1 What percentage of the costs is

a) labour?

b) overheads?

c) materials?

COSTS
Overheads
Labour
Materials

2 23% of marriages at a registry office are between partners who have both been married before.

31% are between partners where only one has been married before.

What percentage of couples have both never been married before?

3 Work out

a) 75% of 600   b) 32% of 550 c) 7.5% of 140

4 Jessica works in a clothes shop. She buys this coat.

She gets a 15% discount. How much does she pay?

£85·00

5 Lucy's sales figures last year were £53 000. Her target this year is an 8% increase.

What is her target figure? (Give your answer to the nearest hundred pounds.)

6 Keith sees the same rucksack on sale in 2 shops.

Which shop is cheaper?

7 Change the fraction to a percentage:

a) $\dfrac{4}{5}$ b) $\dfrac{7}{25}$ c) $\dfrac{5}{8}$ d) $\dfrac{161}{250}$

8 In a spelling test, 30 people are asked to spell 'parallel'.

This is what they write. What percentage get it right?

parallel	parallel	**pareloll**	parallel	**parallel**	parallel	**parallel**	**parallel**	**parallel**	parolell
parallel	**parrallell**	paralel	parallel	parallel	**parallel**	**parallel**	parelol	parelell	**parallel**
paralell	parallel	**parallel**	parralel	**parallel**	parolell	**parolell**	parelel	**parallel**	parolel

9 Becky's recommended daily allowance (RDA) of vitamin C is 60 milligrams.

She drinks a small glass of orange juice which has 20 milligrams in it.

a) Work out what percentage of her RDA this is.

b) How many small glasses of orange juice does she need to drink to obtain 100% of her RDA of vitamin C?

10 A travel agent has four offices.

This bar chart shows the number of skiing holidays booked on Saturday at each office.

a) How many holidays are booked in total?

b) What proportion of these are booked at each office?

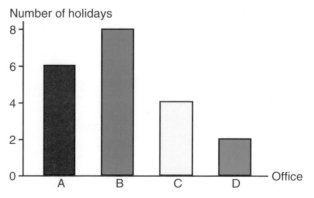

Describe 3 examples of when you have used percentages in other subjects.

Eight

Co-ordinates and graphs

Finding a point

Peter and Jane are taking part in an orienteering competition.

The co-ordinates of the Start are (1, 0).

1 across   0 up

 What are the co-ordinates for the Finish?

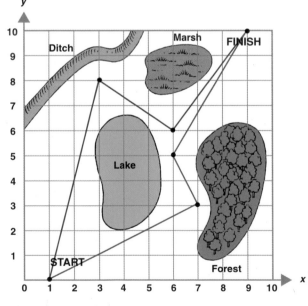

Jane's route is shown in red.

She goes from (1,0) to (3,8) to (6,6) to (9,10).

Peter's route is shown in blue.

 Describe his route by using co-ordinates.

Describe his route by talking about the landmarks.

1 The diagram shows the seating plan of an aircraft and how the seats are 'numbered'.

a) How many seats are there altogether?

b) How can you tell from the seat 'number' on your ticket whether you have a window seat?

c) Give the seat 'numbers' of the seats that are **marked with arrows**.

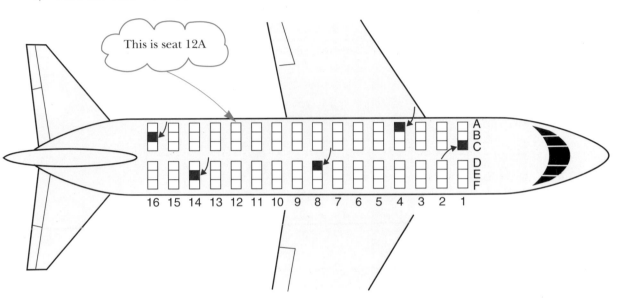

This is seat 12A

2 Write down the co-ordinates of the points A to F on the grid.

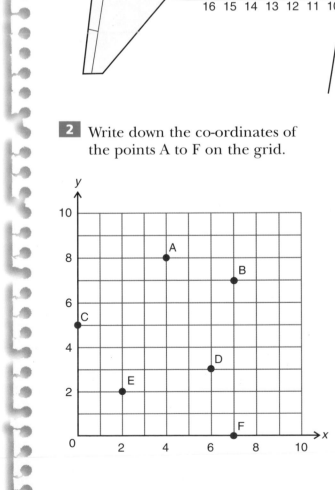

3 Draw a grid with 0 to 10 on each axis.

Join these points.

(1,2) (1,8) (3,8) (3,6) (5,8) (7,8)

(4,5) (7,2) (5,2) (3,4) (3,2)

and back to (1,2).

Shade in the shape you have made.

What letter of the alphabet is it?

A robot is entering your classroom.

Write down a set of instructions that will direct it to the chair furthest from the door.

(Sometimes you see white lines on the floor of factories or warehouses. This is another way to direct robots.)

Positive and negative co-ordinates

Snaefell is the highest point on the Isle of Man.
There is a telecommunications aerial on it.
On the map below, Snaefell is the origin.

Snaefell is (0, 0), Ramsey is (2, 2).

 What about Peel, Port Erin and Douglas?

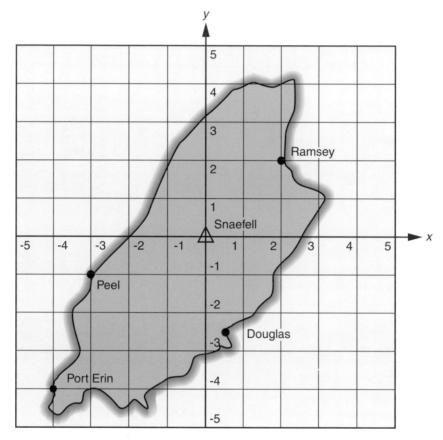

Points on the *x* axis to the left of the origin have negative *x* co-ordinates.

Points on the *y* axis below the origin have negative *y* co-ordinates.

Peel has co-ordinates (−3, −1).

Port Erin is near (−4, −4).

Douglas has co-ordinates (0.5, −2.5).

1 Write down the co-ordinates of points A to H.

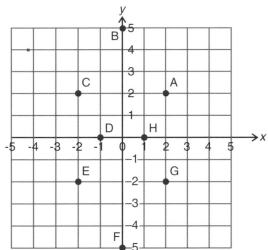

2 Draw a grid with −5 to 5 on each axis.

Join these points.

(3,4)   (5,4)   (5, −3)   (3, −3)

(3,1)   (1, −1)   (−1,1)   (−1, −3)

(−3, −3)   (−3,4)   (−1,4)   (1,2)

and back to (3,4)

Shade in the shape you have made.

What letter of the alphabet is it?

3 Pizza Palace in New York offers a delivery service.

A charge is made for each block travelled.

a) On a piece of squared paper draw a grid like the one in question 1, with Pizza Palace at the origin.

b) Using different coloured pens mark points that are 1 block, 2 blocks, 3 blocks, . . . etc., away from Pizza Palace.

Make lists of the points that you have marked in each group.

For example,

Points 3 blocks away are (−2, −1), . . . etc.

c) Write down a rule to decide if a point is in a particular group.

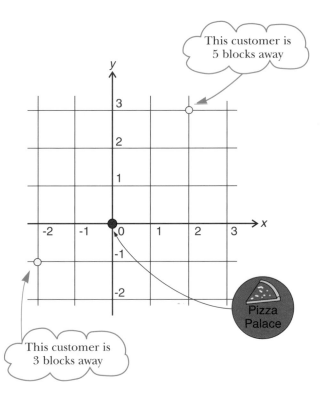

This customer is 5 blocks away

This customer is 3 blocks away

On graph paper, make a scale drawing of the stairs in your school or college.

Think carefully about where you want to have the origin and what scale you want to use.

Give the co-ordinates of the top of each stair.

Equations and graphs

A farmer has 20 metres of fencing.

Here are some of the rectangular pens he can make:

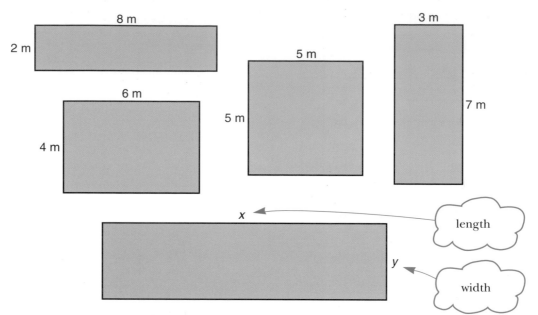

Call the length x and the width y.

The length and the width add up to 10 metres

$$x + y = 10$$

x and y can be these numbers:

x	0	1	2	3	4	5	6	7	8	9	10
y	10	9	8	7	6	5	4	3	2	1	0

These points are plotted on the graph:

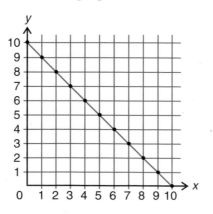

For any of the points on this line $x + y = 10$.

$x + y = 10$ is called the **equation** of the line.

This can also be written as $y = 10 - x$.

1 a) Write down the co-ordinates of the
red points on this grid.

b) Copy and complete this table to
show the *x* and *y* co-ordinates of
the points.

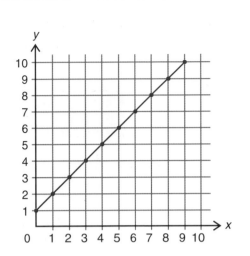

x	0	1	2	3	4	5	6	7	8	9
y										

c) Look carefully at the values of *x*
and *y*. Can you spot the
connection between them? Write it
down in words and symbols.

2 a) (i) Write down the co-ordinates of
the red points on this grid.

(ii) Make a table showing these
values, like the one in
question 1.

(iii) Write down in words and
symbols a connection
between *x* and *y*.

b) Repeat these three steps for the
green points.

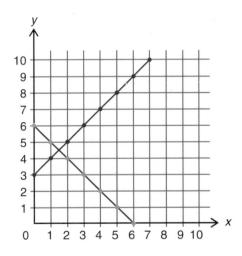

3 A set of points has *y* co-ordinates which are always 2 more than the
x co-ordinate. So when *x* is 0, *y* is 2, and so on.

a) Copy and complete this table.

x	0	1	2	3	4	5	6	7	8
y	2								

b) Mark these points on a grid, as in the diagrams above.

Find out the distance between floors in a large building, such as a
department store or office block.

Draw a graph of the height above ground level (↑) against floor
number (→). Use negative numbers for floors below ground level.

More graphs

Mr Jones has a digital thermometer in his greenhouse.

By moving the switch between °C and °F he can display the temperature in Celsius or Fahrenheit.

This table shows the conversion of temperatures.

°C	0	5	10	15	20	25	30
°F	32	41	50	59	68	77	86

The graph shows the pairs of values of °C and °F plotted on a pair of axes.

Celsius is across and Fahrenheit is up.

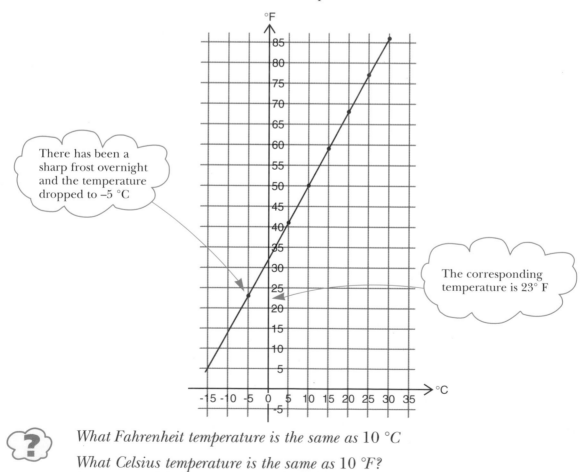

There has been a sharp frost overnight and the temperature dropped to −5 °C

The corresponding temperature is 23° F

What Fahrenheit temperature is the same as 10 °C

What Celsius temperature is the same as 10 °F?

1 Mr Smith has £400 in his bank account.

He takes out £50 every month.

a) Copy and complete this table (x is the number of months and y is the number of pounds in the bank).

x	0	1	2	3	4	5	6	7	8	9	10
y	400	350									

b) Draw a graph to show this information.

c) What happens after 8 months?

d) What happens after 9 and 10 months?

2 Look back at the rectangular enclosures on page 84.

The length is x m and the width is y m, and there is 20 m of fencing altogether.

This table shows some possible values.

x	0	1	2	3	4	5	6	7	8	9	10
y	10	9	8	7	6	5	4	3	2	1	0

This table shows the area, A m^2, of the enclosure for different lengths.

x	0	1	2	3	4	5	6	7	8	9	10
A	0	9	16	21	24	25	24	21	16	9	0

Plot these points on a graph with x on the horizontal axis and A on the vertical axis.

3 a) Copy and complete these tables:

(i) $y = x + 3$

x	–3	–2	–1	0	1	2	3
y							

(ii) $y = 2 - x$

x	–3	–2	–1	0	1	2	3
y							

b) Plot these points on the same axes.
Use **red** for the first table and **blue** for the second table.
Join up the points for each colour.
Where do the 2 lines cross?

Make a cup of coffee, stir it well and record its temperature.

Do the same (stir and record) every 2 minutes for half an hour.

Draw a graph of temperature ($\uparrow$) against time ($\rightarrow$). Comment on its shape.

Finishing off

> ## Now that you have finished this chapter you should be able to
>
> ★ write down the *x* and *y* co-ordinates of a point from a grid
>
> ★ make a table of *x* and *y* from a set of points and look for a simple connection between them
>
> ★ plot a point (*x*, *y*) on a grid
>
> ★ make a table of *x* and *y* from a simple connection between them and draw the points on a grid.

Use the questions in the next exercise to check that you understand everything.

Mixed exercise

1 Write down the co-ordinates of the points A, B and C.

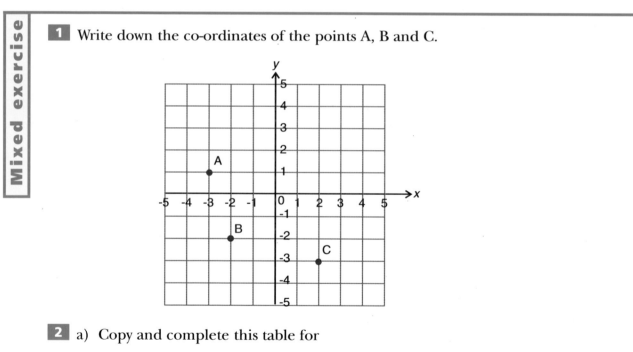

2 a) Copy and complete this table for

$y = 8 - x$

x	0	1	2	3	4	5	6	7	8	9	10
y											

b) Draw a square grid with 0 to 10 on the *x* axis and −2 to 8 on the *y* axis.

c) Mark the points (*x*, *y*) shown in the table.

3 Jane jumps off the high diving board into the pool.
The graph shows the stages of her dive.

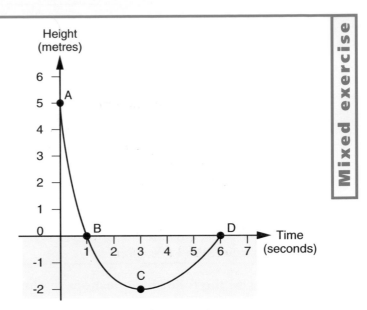

a) What is happening from
 (i) A to B?
 (ii) B to C?
 (iii) C to D?

b) How long after she jumps does Jane hit the water?

c) How far below the surface of the water does Jane dive?

d) How long is she under water?

4 This grid shows the position of a helicopter on a radar screen.

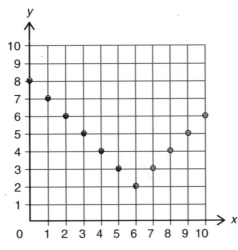

a) What do you think happened at the point (6, 2)?

b) Make two tables to record the x and y co-ordinates, the first table to show the co-ordinates of the red points and the second to show the co-ordinates of the green points.

c) Write down in words and symbols a connection between *x* and *y* for each table.

At the end of a hockey match, Smruti finds that she has lost a gold ring somewhere on the pitch.

All 11 players on her team, and the coach, agree to look for it.

Work out a plan for them to do it systematically.

Nine

Statistics

Use the following questions to check that you still remember these topics.

Revision exercise

1 This pictogram shows the results of a netball team one season.

a) The symbol ◖ means 2 matches.

Draw symbols for 1 match and 3 matches.

b) How many matches did they win, draw and lose?

c) How many matches did they play altogether?

d) Draw a bar chart to show their results.

Win	⬤ ⬤ ⬤ ⬤ ⬤
Draw	⬤ ◖
Lose	⬤ ⬤ ◖
⬤ means 4 matches	

2 Scott puts some bread on his bird table and keeps a record of the birds that eat it. His results are shown in the bar chart.

a) Make a frequency table.

b) How many birds does Scott see in total?

c) What percentage of the birds are starlings?

Type of bird

Blackbirds, Starlings, Magpies, Sparrows, Thrushes, Robins

Frequency: 0 1 2 3 4 5 6

3 Fran stands outside her house and counts the number of people in the first 20 cars that pass by.

1, 3, 4, 1, 4   5, 4, 1, 2, 1   2, 3, 1, 1, 2   3, 3, 2, 1, 6

a) Make a tally chart of the data.

b) Make a frequency table of the data.

c) Draw a vertical line chart to illustrate the data.

4 Ten people work in an office. The numbers of days they are out of the office during one week are as follows.

John 2	Wendy 0	Jenny 0	Karen 0	Roger 2
Stuart 1	Ted 2	Ali 0	Sunil 3	Ray 5

Find

a) the mode   b) the mean

c) the median   d) the range

of the number of days people are absent.

5 Joe is a caretaker for an office.

He must keep the office at a comfortable temperature, not too hot and not too cold.

One day he takes the temperature several times and draws this graph.

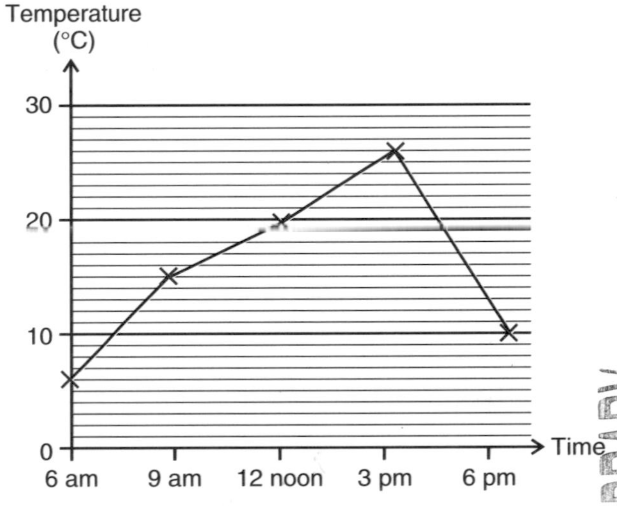

u) How many times does Joe take the temperature?

b) What is the hottest the office gets?

c) Chris is in the office from 9 a.m. to 3 p.m.

What is the coldest the office gets while she is there?

6 Jenny has kept in touch with some of the girls in her class at school.

This vertical line chart shows the number of children they have had.

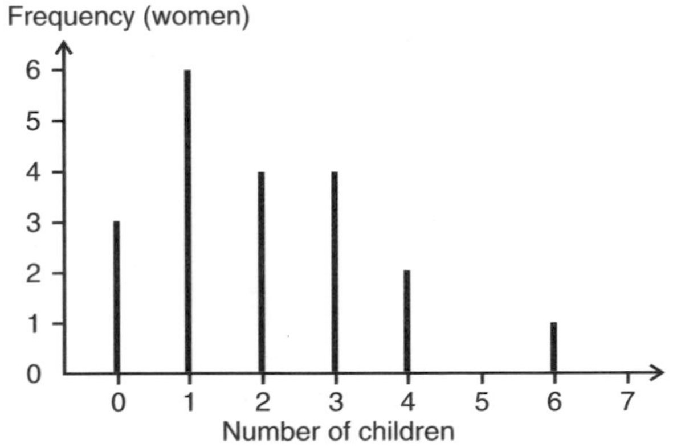

a) How many women does the chart represent?

b) What is the mode of their number of children?

c) What percentage have no children?

d) How many children do they have in total?

e) What is the mean number of children?

Carry out a survey into the sort of shoes your friends like for everyday wear.

Pie charts

Leroy is asked to do a survey to find out how people in his company travel to work.

Here are his results:

Car	Motor-bike	Bicycle	Bus	Train	Walk	Skate-board	Total
90	5	8	15	15	45	2	180

He wants to show this information on a diagram and decides to use a pie chart.

There are 180 people in total and 360° in a full circle.

$$\frac{360°}{180} = 2°$$

So 1 person has 2° on the pie chart.

Leroy sets out his work like this:

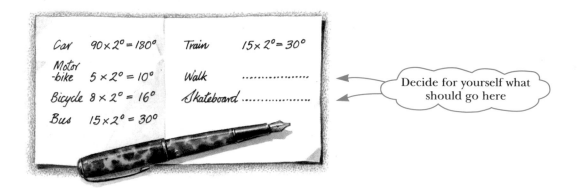

Car   90 × 2° = 180°   Train   15 × 2° = 30°
Motor-bike   5 × 2° = 10°   Walk   ·············
Bicycle   8 × 2° = 16°   Skateboard ···········
Bus   15 × 2° = 30°

Decide for yourself what should go here

Then he draws the pie chart.

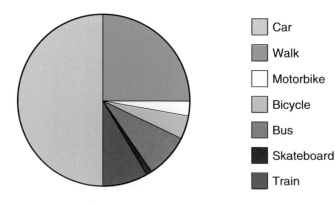

Car
Walk
Motorbike
Bicycle
Bus
Skateboard
Train

 What percentage come by car?

How can you tell this from the pie chart?

What percentage walk?

 Why do you think the company wants to know this information?

1 A clothing company makes £360 000 profit one year. The pie chart shows how this was divided between the children's, teenage and adult departments.

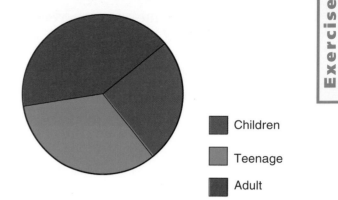

Children

Teenage

Adult

a) Measure the angles in the pie chart.

b) How much profit does each department make?

c) What percentage of the profit comes from teenage clothes?

2 Kevin times some traffic lights near his house.

Colour	Red	Red and amber	Green	Amber
Time in seconds	18	2	12	4

a) Draw a pie chart to show these figures.

b) What percentage of the time are the lights red?

3 This pie chart shows the results for the 36 teams playing in a cricket league one day.

a) How many teams win?

b) How many teams lose?

c) How many teams draw?

d) Why are the angles for Win and Lose the same size?

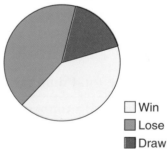

Win

Lose

Draw

4 Anna says that on a typical day she spends her time like this:

Studying   12 hours
Eating   1 hour
Sleeping   8 hours
Relaxing   2 hours
Housework 1 hour

She wants to show this on a pie chart.

a) How many degrees represent 1 hour?

b) Draw the pie chart.

c) What percentage of her time is spent studying?

Do the popular colours for cars change from year to year?

Go round a large car park and record the colour of each car and the registration year letter.

Draw pie charts to compare the results, year by year.

Mean, mode, median and range

20 people enter a fishing competition. The number of fish they catch is shown in the frequency table below. You can also see this information in the vertical line chart.

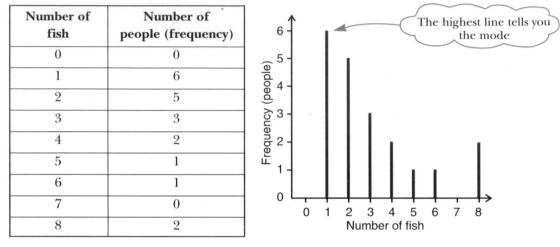

Number of fish	Number of people (frequency)
0	0
1	6
2	5
3	3
4	2
5	1
6	1
7	0
8	2

The highest line tells you the mode

What is a typical number of fish?

Here are three answers you could give.

The **mode** is the most common number of fish, the number with the greatest frequency.

6 people caught 1 fish. The next most common is 2 fish.

The mode is 1.

$$\text{The } \textbf{mean} = \frac{\text{the total number of fish}}{\text{the total number of people}}$$

$$= \frac{0\times0 + 1\times6 + 2\times5 + 3\times3 + 4\times2 + 5\times1 + 6\times1 + 7\times0 + 8\times2}{0 + 6 + 5 + 3 + 2 + 1 + 1 + 0 + 2}$$

A total of 60 fish have been caught by the 20 people in the group

$$= \frac{60}{20} = 3.$$

The middle one when you write the data in order is called the **median**.

number 10   median   number 11

1, 1, 1, 1, 1, 1, 2, 2, 2, 2, 2, 3, 3, 3, 4, 4, 5, 6, 8, 8

The median of 20 is half way between numbers 10 and 11. In this case these are both 2, so the median is 2.

How spread out are the answers? You can measure this by the **range**.

Range = Largest value − Smallest value

In this case Range = 8 − 1 = 7

1 For each of these sets of data, find the mode, median, mean and range.

a) 8, 9, 10, 14, 14

b) 2, 3, 3, 3, 4, 4, 4, 4, 5, 8

c)

Value	0	1	2	3	4
Frequency	2	1	4	1	2

d)

Value	21	22	23	24	25
Frequency	1	1	2	1	1

e)

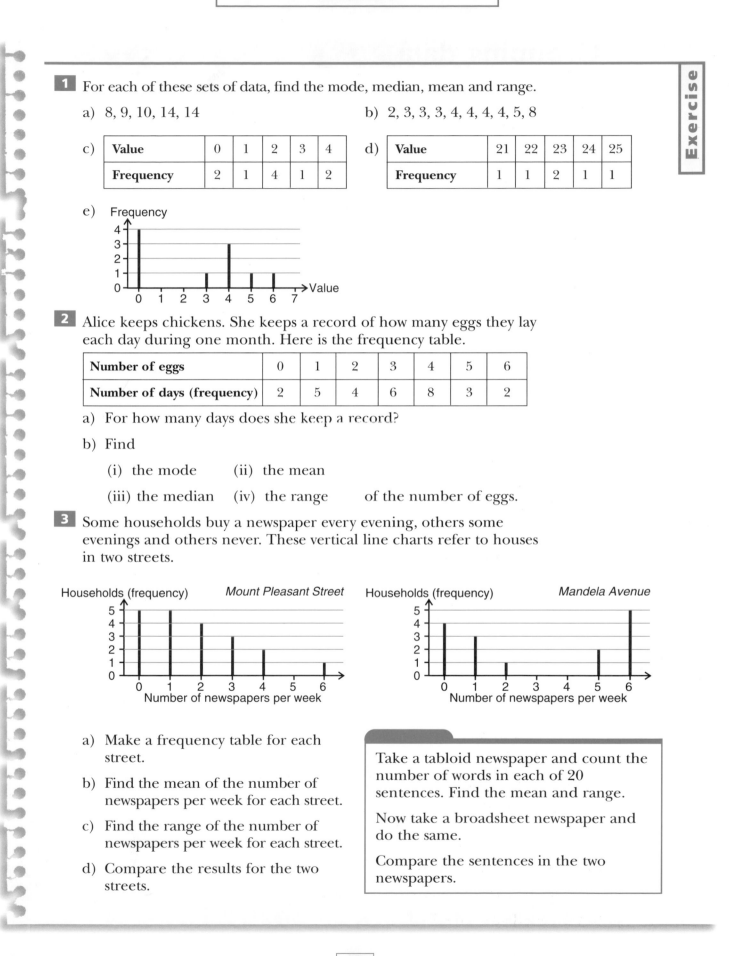

2 Alice keeps chickens. She keeps a record of how many eggs they lay each day during one month. Here is the frequency table.

Number of eggs	0	1	2	3	4	5	6
Number of days (frequency)	2	5	4	6	8	3	2

a) For how many days does she keep a record?

b) Find

    (i) the mode   (ii) the mean

    (iii) the median   (iv) the range   of the number of eggs.

3 Some households buy a newspaper every evening, others some evenings and others never. These vertical line charts refer to houses in two streets.

a) Make a frequency table for each street.

b) Find the mean of the number of newspapers per week for each street.

c) Find the range of the number of newspapers per week for each street.

d) Compare the results for the two streets.

Take a tabloid newspaper and count the number of words in each of 20 sentences. Find the mean and range.

Now take a broadsheet newspaper and do the same.

Compare the sentences in the two newspapers.

Grouping data

Melissa's parents are angry with her. They say she is spending too long on the telephone. One week she makes 20 calls. These are their lengths, in minutes and seconds.

11m 22s	34m 12s	19m 16s	22m 41s	50m 00s
8m 3s	1m 11s	6m 12s	6m 42s	17m 36s
51m 36s	17m 11s	0m 48s	12m 33s	0m 39s
49m 29s	8m 12s	5m 47s	44m 12s	52m 18s

It is quite hard to read data when they are given like this. It is better if they are grouped.

Length (minutes)	0m 0s to 9m 59s	10m 0s to 19m 59s	20m 0s to 29m 59s	30m 0s to 39m 59s	40m 0s to 49m 59s	50m 0s to 59m 59s
Frequency (number of calls)	8	5	1	1	2	3

Melissa says 'Look. Most of my calls are less than 10 minutes.'

Is Melissa correct? What does the frequency table really show?

She draws a frequency chart to make her point.

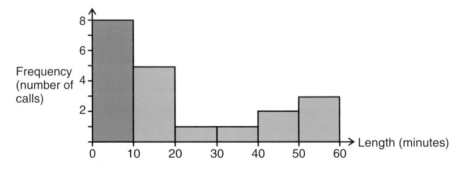

The highest bar is the highest frequency; it is called the **modal class**

Another way of showing these data is the frequency polygon below.

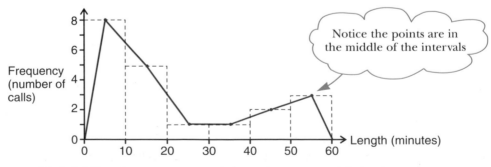

Notice the points are in the middle of the intervals

Do you think Melissa's parents are right to be angry with her?

1 A company is testing a new type of seed. They plant twenty packets each containing 15 seeds and count how many grow.

| 9 | 15 | 1 | 2 | 3 | | 10 | 12 | 13 | 1 | 6 |
| 6 | 11 | 15 | 0 | 1 | | 14 | 13 | 14 | 14 | 1 |

a) The company group the data. Copy and complete this frequency table.

Number of plants growing	0–3	4–7	8–11	12–15
Description	Very low	Low	Medium	High
Frequency				

b) Draw a bar chart.

c) What do you think will happen if the company sells the seeds?

2 Look at the lengths of Melissa's telephone calls.

a) Her total time on the telephone that week was 420 minutes.

How could you have worked this out?

What is the mean length of her 20 calls?

b) How long does she spend on the telephone each day, on average?

c) Melissa's parents make out a new table, with the data grouped like this:

0m 0s to 4m 59s, 5m 0s to 9m 59s, . . ., 55m 0s to 59m 59s

Draw a frequency chart, and draw a frequency polygon on it.

d) What is the modal class now?

To be done as a group.

Find out how good you are at estimating 1 minute. One person says 'Start' and starts timing you. When you think 1 minute is over you say 'Stop'. Group the data and show the results as a frequency chart.

3 The sale prices for 30 cars at an auction are as follows.

£1430	£1750	£2430	£4560	£3480
£2520	£4160	£1995	£2460	£2840
£5100	£3275	£2160	£4050	£5120
£3500	£2750	£1850	£3520	£2650
£1200	£4200	£4000	£5800	£4950
£4510	£3840	£2380	£5750	£4800

Going, going, gone for £4800

a) Make out a tally chart to put the data into groups £0 – £999, £1000 – £1999, £2000 – £2999, and so on.

b) Make a frequency table.

c) Draw a frequency chart and a frequency polygon.

d) Which price range is the modal class?

Scatter diagrams

Nina and her mother are entering a fun run. Nina says, 'You are older than me so you will take longer.'

Is it true that older people usually take longer over a run?

Here are scatter diagrams for three age groups: Time against Age.

You can see three different patterns.

Notice the symbol ⌵. This shows a break in the scale on the axis. Why is it used on the graphs on this page?

In the Juniors the line slopes down.

This is called **negative correlation**.

The greater the age, the less time they take.

In the Adults there is no pattern on the graph.

There is **no correlation**.

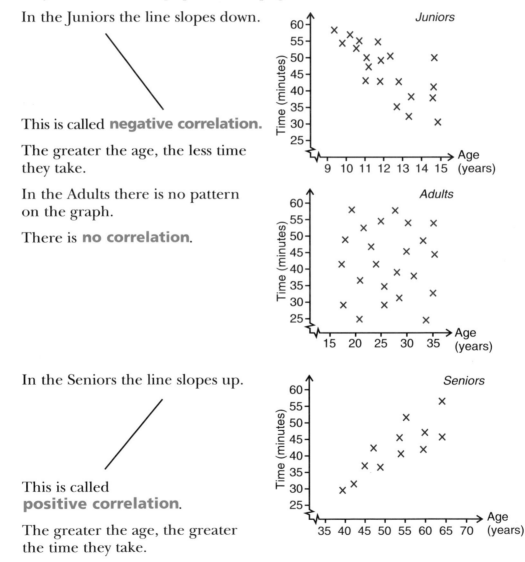

In the Seniors the line slopes up.

This is called **positive correlation**.

The greater the age, the greater the time they take.

When you look for correlation you are looking for an overall pattern. Not all of the points will fit into this pattern.

These graphs are Time against Age. What can you say about Speed against Age?

1 For each of the scatter diagrams (a) to (f) answer 'positive correlation', 'no correlation' or 'negative correlation'.

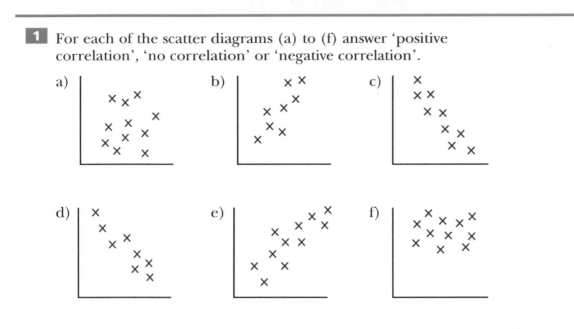

2 A company gives its secretaries a typing test. They all type for one hour. Here is how many pages they type and how many mistakes they make.

Name	Pages	Mistakes	Name	Pages	Mistakes
Sue	4	1	Ali	4	2
Kevin	6	4	Mandy	7	0
Madeleine	5	1	Rus	4	0
Dolly	$3\frac{1}{2}$	0	Savita	$6\frac{1}{2}$	3
Lee	6	2	Linda	5	2

a) Draw a scatter diagram.

b) Describe the correlation and say in simple English what it means.

c) Who is the best typist?

Look at the football league tables.

Draw scatter diagrams of

a) 'Goals for' against 'Points'.

b) 'Goals against' against 'Points'.

Describe any correlation your scatter diagrams show.

Finishing off

> **Now that you have finished this chapter you should be able to**
>
> ★ draw pie charts and frequency polygons
>
> ★ work with mode, median, mean and range
>
> ★ group data
>
> ★ draw scatter diagrams and identify any correlation.

Use the questions in the next exercise to check that you understand everything.

Mixed exercise

1 This pie chart shows the results of a survey of 120 vehicles using a road.

a) How many of each type of vehicle are there?

b) State your answers as percentages.

c) In another survey of 120 vehicles there are 70 cars, 20 lorries, 20 buses and 10 vans.

Draw the pie chart for these figures.

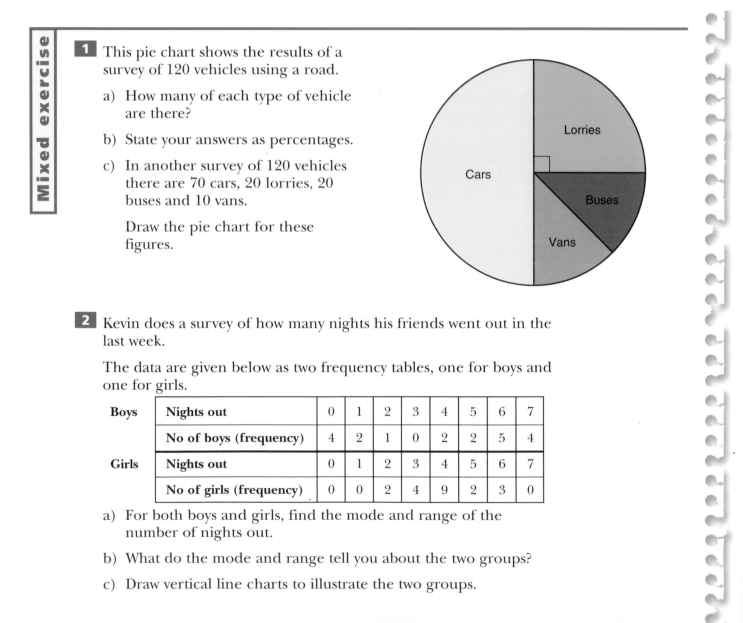

2 Kevin does a survey of how many nights his friends went out in the last week.

The data are given below as two frequency tables, one for boys and one for girls.

Boys	**Nights out**	0	1	2	3	4	5	6	7
	No of boys (frequency)	4	2	1	0	2	2	5	4
Girls	**Nights out**	0	1	2	3	4	5	6	7
	No of girls (frequency)	0	0	2	4	9	2	3	0

a) For both boys and girls, find the mode and range of the number of nights out.

b) What do the mode and range tell you about the two groups?

c) Draw vertical line charts to illustrate the two groups.

3 Denny wants to know if girls pass their driving test sooner than boys. She asks some of her friends how many tests they had to take to pass.

Here are the results.

Girls	Number of tests	1	2	3	4	5	6
	No of girls (frequency)	9	6	3	1	0	1
Boys	Number of tests	1	2	3	4	5	6
	No of boys (frequency)	1	3	6	0	0	0

a) Find the mean and range for the girls.

b) Find the mean and range for the boys.

c) What do these answers tell Denny?

4 Here are the number of days that the 40 employees of a company were absent for sick leave last year.

0	12	2	6	19		0	0	5	8	14
1	2	5	7	0		3	0	1	1	18
6	0	1	1	0		7	0	3	11	0
2	2	0	8	1		0	1	1	14	0

a) Copy and complete this frequency table.

Days absent	0–4	5–9	10–14	15–19
Frequency (no of employees)				

b) Draw a frequency polygon, using the mid-points of the intervals:

2, 7, . . .

c) Describe what this tells you about absenteeism in the company.

5 A new fertiliser is being tried out on some apple trees. The data give the amount of fertiliser used and the fruit yield of each tree.

Fertiliser (g)	Yield (kg)	Fertiliser (g)	Yield (kg)
5	52	12	32
8	40	8	44
6	48	6	46
10	38	5	50
4	50	10	40

a) Plot these data on a scatter diagram. Use the horizontal axis (→) for the Amount of fertiliser. Use the vertical axis (↑) for the Yield.

b) What sort of correlation is there?

c) Do you think it is a good thing to use a lot of fertiliser?

Carry out a survey among your friends to discover whether they think there should be a death penalty.

If yes, for what crimes?

Present your findings as a report.

Ten

Formulae

Before you start this chapter you should be able to

★ put numbers into a formula to solve a problem

★ write down a formula in words and symbols.

Finding a formula

Sonal is getting her holiday photos developed.

She gets 4 sets developed (so she can give some to her friends).

She works out the cost like this:

£5 for my set and 3 lots of £1 for the rest

£5 + 3 × £1 = £8

The formula she uses is

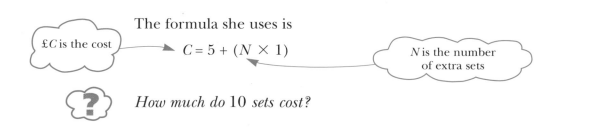

£C is the cost

$$C = 5 + (N \times 1)$$

N is the number of extra sets

? *How much do 10 sets cost?*

Formulae

1 At this car park, how much does it cost for

a) 10 days?   b) 2 weeks?

Airport Car Park
(P)   (P)

1 day	£4
2 days	£8
3 days	£12
4 days	£16
5 days	£20
6 days	£24

2 John opens a bank account.

He put £5 in the bank every week.

The formula for the money in the bank, £M, after W weeks is

$$M = 5 \times W$$

a) How much is in the bank after

(i) 3 weeks?

(ii) 10 weeks?

b) How many weeks does John take to save £100?

3 When Julie puts L litres of petrol in her car, it travel for M miles.

The formula for M is

$$M = 8 \times L$$

Julie puts 5 litres of petrol in her car.

a) How far does it travel for?

b) Each litre of petrol costs 60p.

Write a formula for C, the cost in pence of L litres of petrol.

4 The Post Office works out how much to charge for parcels over 20 kg with this formula:

C stands for the charge in £

$$C = 1.5 \times W - 25$$

W stands for the weight in kg

How much does it cost to post each of these parcels?

a)   b)   c)

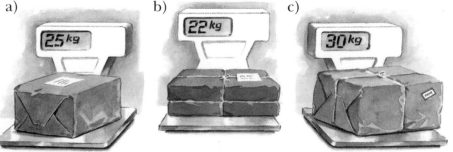

Find 4 formulae that you use in other subjects.

Write them down and explain what the letters in them mean.

Using brackets

Look at this rectangle.

The perimeter is $5 + 3 + 5 + 3 = 16$

You can write this as

the lengths   *the widths*

$2 \times 5 + 2 \times 3$

You can write this neatly using brackets.

$2 \times (5 + 3)$

$2 \times 8 = 16$

You can do the same thing for any rectangle.

The perimeter is $a + b + a + b = 2a + 2b$

You can write this using brackets as $2(a + b)$.

What is the value of $2(a + b)$ when $a = 6$ and $b = 2$?

Always work out what is inside brackets first.

When $a = 6$ and $b = 2$, $2(a + b)$ is

$2 \times (6 + 2) = 2 \times 8 = 16$

$2(a + b)$ means
$2 \times (a + b)$

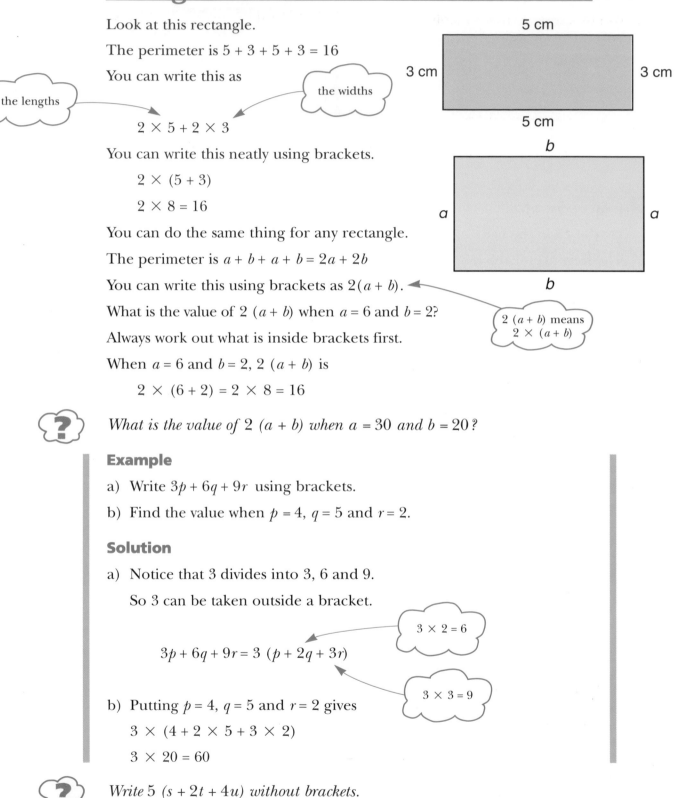

? *What is the value of $2(a + b)$ when $a = 30$ and $b = 20$?*

Example

a) Write $3p + 6q + 9r$ using brackets.

b) Find the value when $p = 4$, $q = 5$ and $r = 2$.

Solution

a) Notice that 3 divides into 3, 6 and 9.

So 3 can be taken outside a bracket.

$3 \times 2 = 6$

$3p + 6q + 9r = 3(p + 2q + 3r)$

$3 \times 3 = 9$

b) Putting $p = 4$, $q = 5$ and $r = 2$ gives

$3 \times (4 + 2 \times 5 + 3 \times 2)$

$3 \times 20 = 60$

? *Write $5(s + 2t + 4u)$ without brackets.*

Formulae

1 Use brackets to write the following formulae more simply.

a) $p = 2l + 2w$ b) $t = 3a + 3b$

2 a) Find the perimeter of this square:

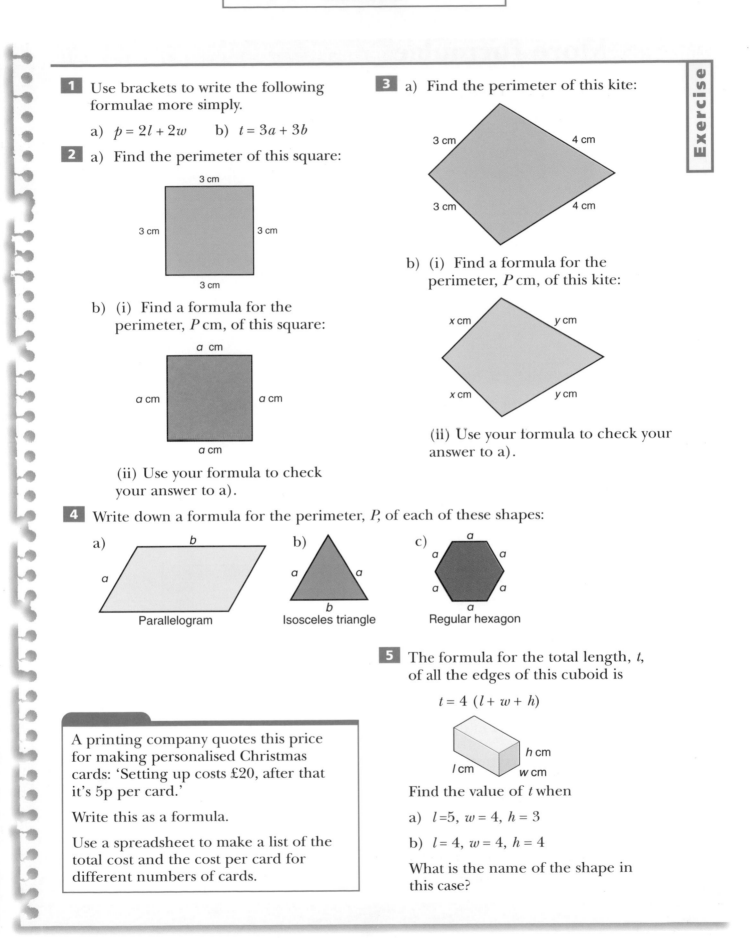

3 cm

3 cm   3 cm

3 cm

b) (i) Find a formula for the perimeter, P cm, of this square:

a cm

a cm a cm

a cm

(ii) Use your formula to check your answer to a).

3 a) Find the perimeter of this kite:

3 cm   4 cm

3 cm   4 cm

b) (i) Find a formula for the perimeter, P cm, of this kite:

x cm y cm

x cm y cm

(ii) Use your formula to check your answer to a).

4 Write down a formula for the perimeter, P, of each of these shapes:

a)

b

a

Parallelogram

b)

a a

b

Isosceles triangle

c)

a

a a

a a

a

Regular hexagon

A printing company quotes this price for making personalised Christmas cards: 'Setting up costs £20, after that it's 5p per card.'

Write this as a formula.

Use a spreadsheet to make a list of the total cost and the cost per card for different numbers of cards.

5 The formula for the total length, t, of all the edges of this cuboid is

$$t = 4 (l + w + h)$$

h cm

l cm w cm

Find the value of t when

a) $l = 5$, $w = 4$, $h = 3$

b) $l = 4$, $w = 4$, $h = 4$

What is the name of the shape in this case?

More formulae

To find the area of this rectangle you multiply the length by the width.

$$A = 4 \times 3 = 12$$

area

So the area is 12 cm^2.

You can do this for any rectangle.

$$A = a \times b$$

You can write $a \times b$ as ab without the $\times$ sign.

For a square the formula is

$$A = a \times a$$

You normally write this as a^2.

This is a power, you say 'a squared'

Look at these two rectangles:

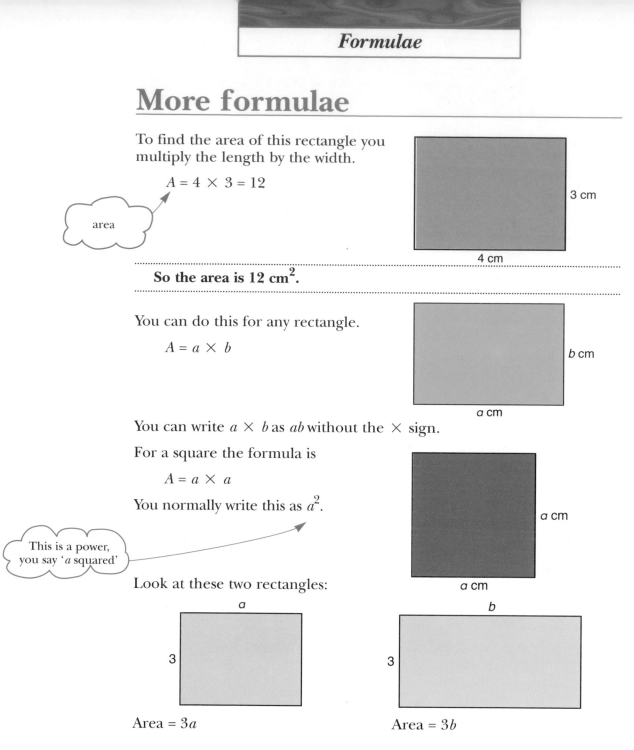

Area = $3a$ Area = $3b$

So the total area is $3a + 3b$.

But you can think of these as one big rectangle, like this:

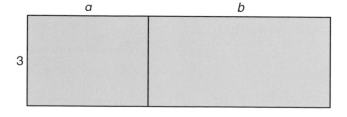

and write the area as $3(a+b)$.

1 Find the value of $2x + 2y$ when.

   a) $x = 3$ and $y = 4$

   b) $x = 5$ and $y = 1$

   c) $x = 10$ and $y = 5$

2 Find the value of xy when

   a) $x = 4$ and $y = 4$

   b) $x = 3$ and $y = 1$

3 Find the value of $2(x + y)$ when

   a) $x = 3$ and $y = 4$ b) $x = 5$ and $y = 1$ c) $x = 10$ and $y = 5$

4 a) Find a formula for the area of this rectangle:

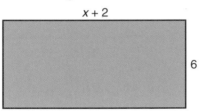

   b) Find the area when $x = 10$.

5 This cube has edges which are a cm long.

   a) Find formulae for

     (i) the volume

     (ii) the surface area.

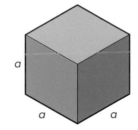

   b) Find the volume and surface area when $a = 2$.

6 a) Find a formula for the area of this letter L.

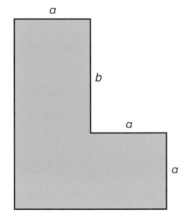

   b) Find the area when $a = 2$ and $b = 3$.

7 The formula for the area of a triangle, A, is

$$A = \frac{1}{2} \times \text{base} \times \text{height}$$

   a) Find a formula for the area of this triangle:

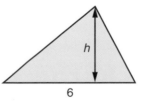

   b) Find the area when $h = 4$.

Find out how a taxi fare is worked out for short journeys with no delays.

Explain it in words and write it as a formula.

Finishing off

> **Now that you have finished this chapter you should be able to**
>
> ★ write down a formula in words and symbols
>
> ★ collect like terms to simplify a formula
>
> ★ put numbers into a formula to solve a problem
>
> ★ use brackets.

Use the questions in the next exercise to check that you understand everything.

1 Work out $x + y$ when

   a) $x = 7$ and $y = 4$ b) $x = 8$ and $y = 2$ c) $x = 12$ and $y = 0$

2 Work out ab when

   a) $a = 5$ and $b = 7$ b) $a = 2$ and $b = 6$ c) $a = 3$ and $b = 9$

3 Work out x^2 when

   a) $x = 1$ b) $x = 3$ c) $x = 5$

4 The mean of two numbers is found by adding them together and dividing the answer by two.

   a) Find the means of

      (i) 2 and 4

      (ii) 6 and 10.

   b) Write a formula to find the mean, M, of two numbers P and Q.

5

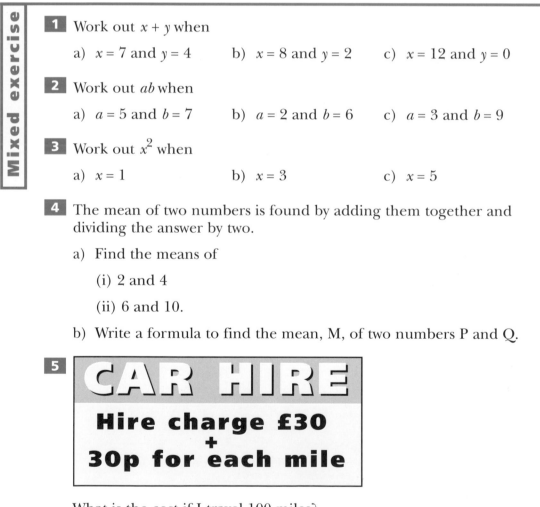

CAR HIRE
Hire charge £30
+
30p for each mile

What is the cost if I travel 100 miles?

Write a formula for the cost, £C, for M miles.

6 Write the following without brackets:

a) $5(a + b)$
b) $2(x - y)$
c) $3(x + 3y)$

7 Write the following with brackets:

a) $3a + 3b$
b) $4x - 4y$
c) $2x + 6y$

8 The cost £C of having T of these cards printed is given by the formula

$C = T + 5$

How much does it cost for

a) 2 cards?
b) 10 cards?
c) 20 cards?

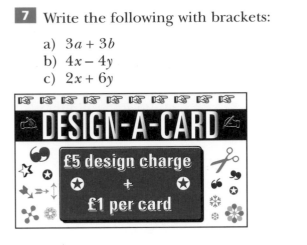

9 Four members of a tennis club share out the tennis balls there like this:

there are B balls in each box

Each of them has one full box containing B balls, plus 3 spare balls.

a) Which of these formulae gives the total number of balls, N?

A $N = 4B + 3$

B $N = 4B + 12$

C $N = (4 + 3) B$

b) At the end of the day, the friends count the balls.

There are 36 of them.

Someone says 'This means that $B = 6$'.

Is she right?

How do you know?

Different car hire companies work out the charge in different ways. Get information from a number of companies.

In each case write the charge in words and as a formula.

Think of a trip away (such as 2 days and 500 miles) and use your formulae to work out the cheapest company for the trip.

Eleven

Money

★ This chapter looks at ideas you first met in Book 1.

★ Make sure you really understand them before you go on to the new work.

Pay

Danny is paid £5 an hour.

He works 37 hours a week.

He gets  wages

$37 \times £5 = £185$ a week.

How much does Danny get a year?

He gets £185 every week, and there are 52 weeks in a year.

$52 \times £185 = £9620$  salary

Danny might get more than this if he does overtime, or works on Bank Holidays.

On Bank Holidays, Danny gets 'time and a half'.

This means he gets $1\frac{1}{2}$ times the normal rate.

$1\frac{1}{2} \times £5 = £7.50$ so he gets £7.50 an hour on Bank Holidays.

One week Danny gets 10% commission on everything he sells.

He sell items worth £900.

How much commission does he get?

 10% of 900

$= \dfrac{10}{100} \times 900$

$= \dfrac{9000}{100} = 90$

He gets £90 commission.

1 Work out the wages for

a) 35 hours at £10 an hour   b) 3 days work at £60 a day

c) 40 hours at £5 an hour   d) 30 hours at £7.50 an hour.

2 Work out the wages for each person.

a) April works 35 hours and gets £6.50 an hour.

b) Jack works 40 hours at £5 an hour, and does 5 hours' overtime at 'time and a half'.

c) Ravi works 4 days and gets £80 a day.

3 Ken keeps this record of when he works.

a) How many hours does Ken work a week?

b) He gets £6 an hour during the week and 'double time' (£12) at weekends.

How much does Ken get?

Mon	6 hours
Tues	
Wed	4 hours
Thur	8 hours
Fri	7 hours
Sat	
Sun	4 hours

4 Work out the salary for each person.

a) Sadie earns £900 a month.

b) Robin earns £750 a month.

c) Lilly earns £1100 a month.

5 Pat gets this job.

a) How much does she get each month?

b) After a year Pat gets a 5% rise.

How much extra does she get each month?

Office Manager

Salary £18,000

Apply to P.O.Box 219

6 Sanjit earns £800 a month and also gets 20% commission on everything he sells.

Here are his sales figures for April to July.

April	May	June	July
£1000	£1090	£970	£760

Work out Sanjit's pay for each of these months.

Look at job adverts in a newspaper or job centre. Choose 3 jobs, one with high pay, one with lower pay and one in the middle.

For each job, estimate
a) the pay per hour
b) the pay per week
c) the pay per year.

Tax

Jo's salary is £8000. This is her **gross salary**

She does not get all this money.

She has to pay **tax**

To see how this is calculated, look at this diagram. (Each square is £1000.)

No tax is paid on the first £3000

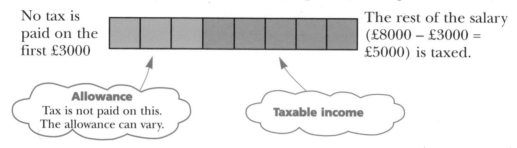

The rest of the salary (£8000 – £3000 = £5000) is taxed.

Allowance
Tax is not paid on this. The allowance can vary.

Taxable income

Jo pays tax at 20 pence for every pound of her taxable income.

She pays 20% of £5000

$= \dfrac{20}{100} \times £5000$

$= £1000$

20p for every pound or 20p in the pound is the same as 20%

Jo pays £1000 tax.

She keeps the rest of her salary.

The money she keeps is called the **net salary**

tax

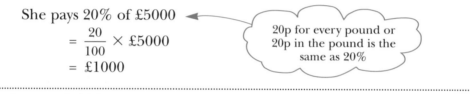

net salary

Jo's net salary is £7000.

Jo's sister gets £13 000 salary. What is her net salary?

She works it out like this:

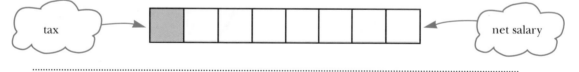

taxable income = £13 000 – £3000
= £10 000
tax is 20% of £10 000
$\dfrac{20}{100} \times$ 10 000
$= \dfrac{200000}{100} = 2000$ so £2000 tax
Net salary = gross salary – tax
= £13000 – £2000 = £11 000

So her net salary is £11 000.

1 Work out the taxable income for a salary of:

a) £9000 with an allowance of £3000

b) £12 000 with an allowance of £4000

c) £18 000 with an allowance of £3000.

2 Work out the tax paid on a taxable income of:

a) £16 000 at 20p in the pound

b) £15 000 at 25p in the pound

c) £12 000 at 22p in the pound.

3 Stewart is a chef.

His salary is £16 000, and his allowance is £3000.

a) What is his taxable income?

He pays tax at 20p in the pound.

b) How much tax does he pay?

c) What is his net salary?

4 Poppy sees these two jobs.

The allowance for both of them is £4000.

Tax is paid at 25p in the pound for both of them.

a) Work out the net salary for each job.

b) How much more is the net salary of the second job?

£15,000

Telesales
£14,000

Marketing
£16,000

5 Julie's allowance is £3000.

She pays tax at 25p in the pound.

Julie says 'I only want the job if the net salary is more than £15 000.'

Does Julie want the job?

Computer Engineer
£24 K
Apply within

Find out the allowance for a single person and the rates of tax.

Use your figures to work out the net salary for each of the jobs you found for the activity on page 111.

Value for money?

Anna wants to buy a computer.

There are a number of ways she can do this.

Buy now, pay later

Anna sees the computer she wants in the first shop.

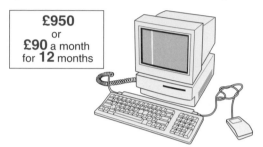

£950
or
£90 a month
for **12** months

She does not have enough money to buy it.

How much does it cost her to pay over 12 months?

How much more is this than the cash price?

VAT (Value Added Tax)

Anna goes into another shop.
She sees the same computer.

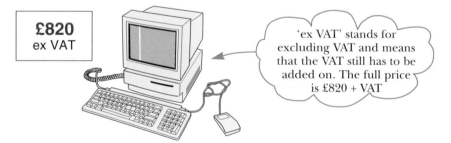

£820
ex VAT

'ex VAT' stands for excluding VAT and means that the VAT still has to be added on. The full price is £820 + VAT

The present rate of VAT is 17.5%.

How much does the computer cost in this shop?

$$17.5\% \text{ of } 820 = \frac{17.5}{100} \times 820$$
$$= 143.5$$

The VAT is £143.50

Total cost = Cost + VAT

= £820 + £143.50

= £963.50

So in this shop, the computer costs £963.50.

What would you advise Anna to do?

1 For each item, work out

   a) the total cost over 36 months

   b) the extra amount paid.

£595 or £20 a month for 36 months

£995 or £90 deposit + £30 a month for 36 months

2 VAT is to be added on to these items at 17.5%.

£30

£20

£150

   Work out

   a) the amount of VAT

   b) the price including VAT.

3 In 'Pricebeaters' a TV is priced at £200 ex VAT.

   In 'TV World' it is priced at £230 inc VAT.

   Which shop is cheaper, and by how much when

   a) the rate of VAT is 17.5%?

   b) the rate of VAT is 15%?

Some computer stores show prices 'ex VAT'.

Why do you think they do this?

Go to a computer store and find four different computers with 'ex VAT' prices.

Work out the full price of each computer.

Profit and loss

Janet owns a clothes shop.

She buys denim jackets for £50 and makes £20 profit when she sells them.

profit

cost price

£50 + £20 = £70 ← selling price

She sells the jackets for £70.

One of the jackets is ripped, so she sells it for £40.

How much does she make on this one?

loss

cost price

£50 − £10 = £40 ← selling price

She makes a loss of £10 on this jacket.

Jan's jackets £70

Percentage profit

You can work out the **percentage profit** like this:

$$\textbf{Percentage profit} = \frac{\textbf{profit}}{\textbf{cost price}} \times \textbf{100}$$

So for the denim jackets,

$$\text{percentage profit} = \frac{20}{50} \times 100$$

profit

cost price

$$= 40$$

The profit is 40%.

Now Janet buys some leather jackets for £300.

She wants to make 40% profit on them.

$$40\% \text{ of } 300 = \frac{40}{100} \times 300$$
$$= 120$$

So to get £120 profit, she has to price them at

£300 + £120 = £420

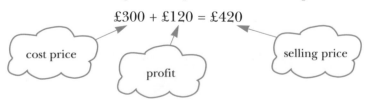

cost price

profit

selling price

1 Work out the selling price when

a) the cost price is £10 and the profit is £5

b) the cost price is £60 and the profit is £10

c) the cost price is £50 and the loss is £20.

2 Work out the profit or loss when

a) the cost price is £40 and the selling price is £50

b) the cost price is £100 and the selling price is £90

c) the cost price is £7 and the selling price is £10.

3 The cost price of this skirt is £25.

£40

What is

a) the profit?

b) the percentage profit?

4 The cost price of this book is £6.

What is

a) the profit?

b) the percentage profit?

5 Zoe buys 20 mugs at £4 each.

She sells 16 of them for £6 each.

The other 4 are chipped and she sells them for £2 each.

a) How much does she get altogether?

b) What is her total profit?

c) What is the percentage profit?

6 A painting is bought for £25 and sold at 25% profit.

a) What is the profit?

b) What is the selling price?

7 Lana pays £3000 for a car.

Next year, she sells it for £2400.

a) What is her loss?

b) What is her percentage loss?

> Look at a long list of 2nd hand car prices. Choose a common model of car and make a list of prices of this type of car. What percentage of its value does this type of car lose each year?

Finishing off

Use the questions in the next exercise to check that you understand everything.

Mixed exercise

1 Linda earns £7 an hour and works 36 hours a week.

a) How much does she earn each week?

b) She gets a 4% pay rise. How much extra does she get each week?

2 Ravi is paid £6.50 an hour and works 38 hours a week.

This week he does 3 hours' overtime and is paid 'double time'.

How much is he paid altogether this week?

3 Vicki gets this job.

This table shows her sales in her first 3 months.

Month	Sept	Oct	Nov
Sales	£2000	£2400	£2250

a) Work out her commission each month.

b) Work out her pay each month.

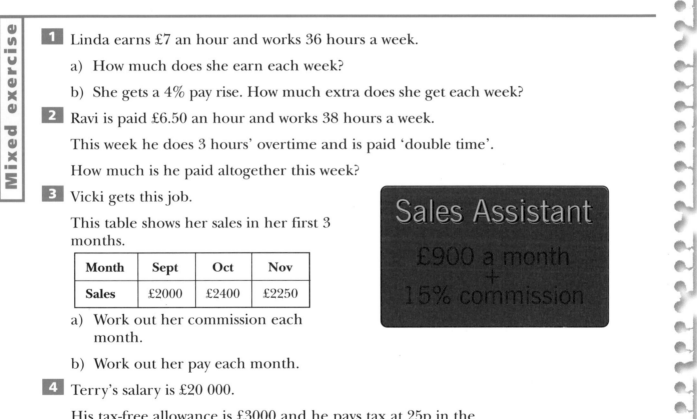

Sales Assistant

£900 a month
+
15% commission

4 Terry's salary is £20 000.

His tax-free allowance is £3000 and he pays tax at 25p in the pound.

a) What is Terry's taxable income?

b) How much tax does he pay?

c) What is his net salary?

d) Terry gets a pay rise of £5000.

How much extra tax does he pay?

5 Steve buys this washing machine and pays over 36 months.

£1485 or £50 a month for 36 months

a) How much does he pay altogether?

b) How much more than the cash price is this?

7 Jamie is selling some of his things.

FOR ●SALE
skateboard £20
tennis racket £15
bike   £70
all in good condition. see
Jamie in room 19A.

a) The skateboard cost him £30.

   (i) How much loss does he make?

   (ii) What is the percentage loss?

b) The tennis racket cost him £10.

   (i) How much profit does he make?

   (ii) What is the percentage profit?

c) The bike cost him £150.

   (i) How much loss does he make?

   (ii) What is the percentage loss?

6 Jed sees these CD players in two different shops.

£236 ex 17·5% VAT

£279 inc VAT

Which one is cheaper, and by how much?

8 Emma buys 20 footballs at £5 each.

She prices them so that she makes 40% profit.

a) How much profit does she make on each ball?

b) What is the selling price?

Emma sells 18 balls at this price.

The other two are damaged and she sells them for £3 each.

c) How much does she get for all 20 balls?

d) What is her total profit?

e) What is her percentage profit on the whole deal?

Use a spreadsheet to make a table with these headings.

Item	Price (ex VAT)	VAT	Price (inc VAT)

Find out the price (ex VAT) of 8 electrical items and add on VAT at the current rate to get the price (inc VAT).

Twelve

Equations

★ This chapter looks at new ideas.

★ It is about unknowns and equations and how you can use them to solve problems.

Unknowns

Look at this equation:

$$3 \times \square = 18$$

There is an unknown number in here

? *What number goes in the box?*

In algebra a letter is used to stand for the **unknown**

We can use a letter, such as *x*, instead of the box.

Then we get this **equation**

$$3 \times x = 18$$

You can write this as
$3x = 18$

When you multiply this by 3, you get 18

....

3 × 6 = 18 so the answer is 6.

....

The two sides balance.

Look at this mobile.

It is balanced

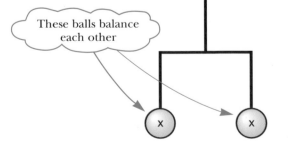

These balls balance each other

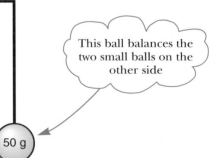

This ball balances the two small balls on the other side

x   x   50 g

? *What does each small ball weigh?*

How can you write this as an equation?

Equations

1 Fill in the missing numbers in these equations:

 a) $\square \times 2 = 8$

 b) $7 \times \square = 21$

 c) $\square \times 9 = 90$

2 Find the weight of the letters on these mobiles.

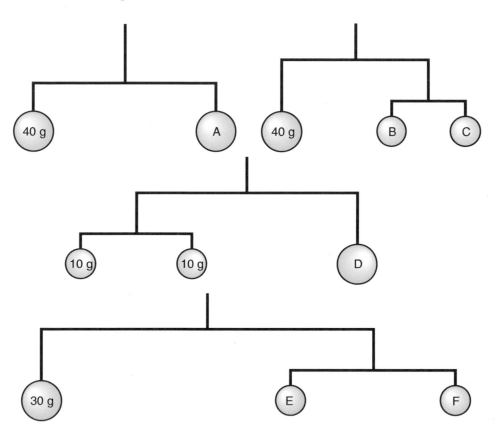

3 a) Fill in the missing numbers in these equations:

 (i) $\square + 8 = 12$

 (ii) $7 + \square = 13$

 (iii) $\square - 9 = 5$

 b) Write out each equation with x instead of the box.

Design a mobile of your own to be made out of cardboard.

Be careful to check that every part of it balances.

Make the mobile.

Solving equations

Look at this picture.

The bag contains an unknown number of marbles.

The bag plus one marble on one side balances 4 marbles on the other side

The bag is very light, and does not weigh anything on these scales

Solve

$x + 1 = 4$

This is an equation.

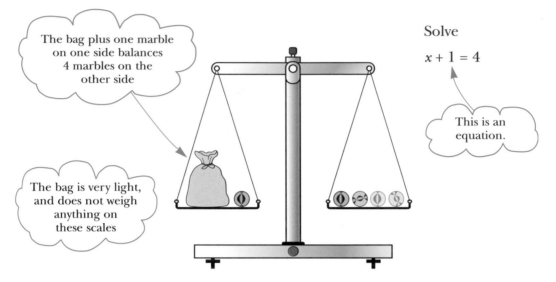

What happens when you take a marble from both sides?

The bag balances 3 marbles

Solution

Subtract 1 from each side.

$x + 1 - 1 = 4 - 1$

$x = 3$

This is the solution of the equation.

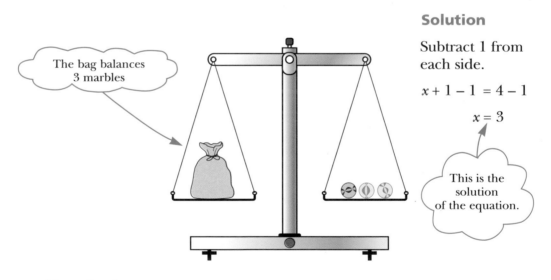

Now check your answers.

There are $3 + 1 = 4$ marbles on the left.

There are 4 marbles on the right.

It balances, so $x = 3$ is correct.

1 Work out how many marbles are in each bag.

a)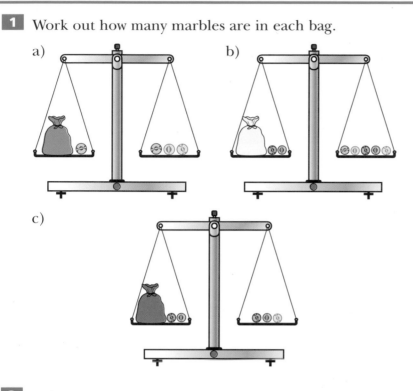

b)

c)

2 Solve these equations by subtracting the same number from both sides. Check your answers.

a) $x + 1 = 3$

b) $x + 2 = 5$

c) $x + 1 = 11$

d) $x + 5 = 6$

3 Solve these equations by adding the same number to both sides. Check your answers.

a) $x - 1 = 2$

b) $x - 2 = 6$

c) $x - 5 = 1$

d) $x - 3 = 10$

Find out how the scoring works in snooker, if you don't already know.

A snooker player scores 12 points in a 5-ball break. List all the different ways in which this can happen.

More equations

To solve an equation, you need to get just the unknown on one side.

Always do the same thing to both sides when you solve an equation.

How do you solve $2x = 10$?

This is how Nat does it:

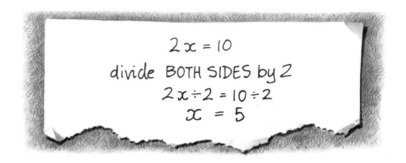

$2x = 10$
divide BOTH SIDES by 2
$2x \div 2 = 10 \div 2$
$x = 5$

Sometimes you have to start by tidying up the unknown terms.

The equation $5x - 3x = 10$ is the same as $2x = 10$. Nat has solved this equation above.

Sometimes it takes more than one step to get just the unknown on one side.

At each step, you need to do the same thing to both sides.

How do you solve $2x + 1 = 9$?

Nat does it like this:

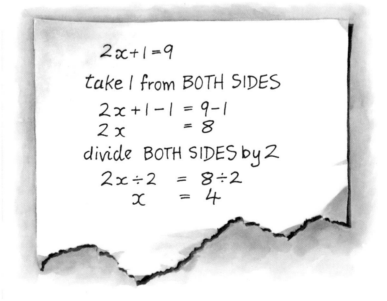

$2x + 1 = 9$
take 1 from BOTH SIDES
$2x + 1 - 1 = 9 - 1$
$2x \qquad = 8$
divide BOTH SIDES by 2
$2x \div 2 = 8 \div 2$
$x \qquad = 4$

Is Nat correct? Check by putting $x = 4$ in the left side.

You get $2 \times 4 + 1 = 8 + 1 = 9$.

It is the same as the right side, so Nat is correct.

Equations

1 Solve these equations by dividing both sides by the same number.

a) $2x = 6$

b) $3x = 9$

c) $2x = 20$

d) $10x = 20$

2 Solve these equations by doing the same thing to both sides.

a) $x + 6 = 10$

b) $x - 3 = 2$

c) $5x = 15$

d) $7x = 14$

3 Solve these equations. Check your answers.

a) $2x + 1 = 9$ e) $4x - 1 = 11$

b) $3x - 5 = 10$ f) $3x + 2 - 20$

c) $5x - 2 = 8$ g) $5x + 4 = 39$

d) $6x + 3 = 15$ h) $2x - 1 = 4$

4 This equilateral triangle has a perimeter of 12 cm.

This can be written as $3x = 12$.

Find the length of each side by solving the equation.

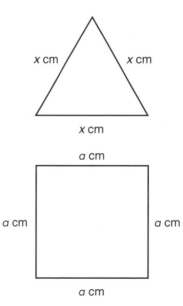

x cm x cm

x cm

5 This square has a perimeter of 20 cm.

a) Write this fact as an equation.

b) Find the length of each side by solving the equation.

a cm

a cm a cm

a cm

Working with a partner write some statements with missing numbers and challenge you partner to find the missing numbers.

Trial and improvement

Ann thinks of a number between 1 and 100. Rachel tries to guess it.

Ann says 'too big' or 'too small' until Rachel gets it right.

This method is called **trial and improvement**. You often use it in everyday life.

When you run a bath, you use the hot and cold taps. You turn each one, a bit more hot or a bit more cold, until the water is the right temperature.

? *Think of some more everyday trial and improvement situations.*

Example

A square lawn has area 200 m^2.

Without using your calculator,
find the length, x m, of the sides,
to the nearest whole number.

200 m^2 | x m

x m

Solution

The area is $x \times x$ or x^2. So you need to solve the equation

$$x^2 = 200$$

Try $x = 10$: $10^2 = 100$ so 10 is too small.

Try $x = 20$: $20^2 = 400$ so 20 is too big.

Try $x = 15$: $15^2 = 225$ so 15 is too big but getting close.

You know x is between 10 and 20

Try $x = 14$: $14^2 = 196$ so 14 is too small but very close.

This is the answer you want

The sides of the lawn are 14 m long (to the nearest whole number).

? *How can you use your calculator to check your answer?*

1 Charlotte is 4 years older than Tom. Their ages add up to 20.

a) Sean tries to work out their ages.

Sean says, "If Tom is 6, Charlotte is 10 and that makes 16. That's not right."
How should Sean continue?

b) You can make this problem into an equation. Using

t = Tom's age

and $t + 4$ = Charlotte's age

The equation is $t + t + 4 = 20$

Solve this equation.

2 Phil has a recipe for marmalade.

It says, "For every lemon, use 5 oranges."

Phil tells his daughter, Fiona, "I have bought 30 pieces of fruit. How many lemons and how many oranges?"

a) Fiona says, "If Dad has 1 lemon he has 5 oranges, so that's 6 altogether. That's not enough, so…"
How should Fiona continue?

b) You can make this question into an equation. Using

l = the number of lemons
and $5l$ = the number of oranges

the equation is $l + 5l = 30$
Solve this equation.

3 Two small animals arrive on an island. They breed. After 1 year, there are 4 of them. After 2 years, there are 8 of them, and so on.

Work out how many years it takes for there to be

a) one thousand of them

b) one million of them.

4 Find two numbers such that:

- one number is 5 more than the other

- when they are multiplied together the answer is 2250.

Try out the 'Think of a number' game on the opposite page with a partner.

How many goes did you need?

Can you do it quicker next time?

Is there any skill involved?

Finishing off

Now that you have finished this chapter you should

★ understand the terms unknown and equation

★ be able to use a method to solve equations such as $2x + 1 = 5$

★ be able to use trial and improvement to solve equations.

Use the questions in the next exercise to check that you understand everything.

Mixed exercise

1 Fill in the missing numbers.

a) $\square \times 5 = 35$

b) $7 \times \square = 63$

c) $\square \times 4 = 36$

2 Find the unknowns in this sum.

$$
\begin{array}{r}
4\ 7\ \square \\
+\ 1\ \square\ 6 \\
\hline
\square\ 2\ 9 \\
\end{array}
$$

3 Solve these equations by subtracting the same number from both sides.

a) $x + 4 = 11$

b) $x + 7 = 40$

c) $x + 12 = 24$

d) $x + 6 = 18$

4 Solve these equations by adding the same number to both sides.

a) $x - 3 = 7$

b) $x - 1 = 2$

c) $x - 8 = 30$

d) $x - 13 = 11$

5 Solve these equations by dividing both sides by the same number.

a) $2x = 12$

b) $5x = 25$

c) $9x = 18$

d) $10x = 40$

6 Solve these equations by doing the same thing to both sides.

a) $x + 15 = 35$

b) $x - 12 = 17$

c) $7x = 707$

7 The product of two numbers is 408. One number is 7 larger than the other.

Find the numbers.

8 Sally is using trial and improvement to solve

$$x^2 = 11$$

This is how she starts:

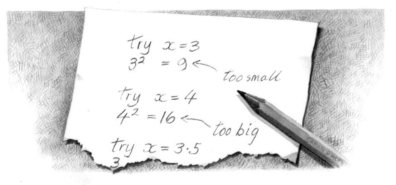

Finish off her working to find the solution to 1 decimal place.

Look in a cookery book for a recipe for roasting a chicken. You will find that the cooking time depends on the weight of the bird. Write out the instructions in words and as a formula.

Give some examples of how you use the formula.

A chicken takes 2 hours to cook: how big is it?

Thirteen

Ratio and proportion

Before you start this chapter you should be able to

★ change simple fractions into decimals

★ change simple fractions into percentages.

Proportion

'Pea green' paint is made by mixing yellow and blue.

> **MIXING INSTRUCTIONS**
>
> ■ 3 parts yellow to 1 part blue

For example, 3 tins of yellow are mixed with 1 tin of blue.

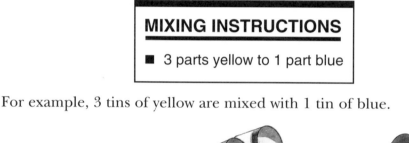

3 parts yellow to 1 part blue

? *How many tins of each colour do you need for twice as much pea green?*

Just double the number of tins

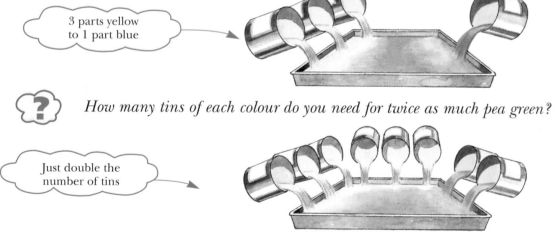

3 parts to 1 part is the same ratio as 6 parts to 2 parts.

3 parts to 1 part is written 3:1.

 What other statements are the same as 3:1?
How many tins of yellow go with 5 tins of blue?
How many tins of blue go with 30 tins of yellow?

The amount of yellow is $\frac{3}{4}$ or 75% or 0.75.

 What fraction of the tins are blue?
What is this as a percentage and as a decimal?

1 'Purple Haze' paint is made by mixing red and blue.

> ### MIXING INSTRUCTIONS
>
> - 2 parts red to 1 part blue

a) How many tins of blue do you mix with 4 tins of red?

b) How many tins of red do you mix with 5 tins of blue?

2 A recipe for scones uses 4 parts of flour to 1 part of butter.

a) How much flour is mixed with 50 grams of butter?

b) How much butter is mixed with 300 grams of flour?

3 Linda and Jane agree to pay the phone bill in the ratio 2:1.

a) Linda pays £120. How much does Jane pay?

b) What fraction of the bill does Jane pay?

4 This pie chart shows Mr Singh's sales of local newspapers on Tuesday. He sells 20 copies of The Weekly.

a) What is the ratio of sales of The Weekly to The News?

b) How many copies of The News does he sell?

On Friday Mr Singh sells 100 copies of The Weekly. The ratio of sales is the same as for Tuesday.

c) How many copies of The News does he sell on Friday?

d) Why do you think he sells five times as many local newspapers on a Friday?

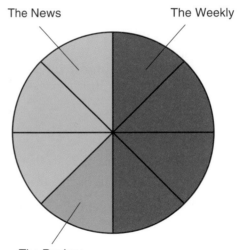

The News   The Weekly

The Review

Go into a DIY store that has a machine for mixing paint.
How does it work?
Give examples of 3 colours that can be mixed.
State the proportions of the different colours in the mixtures.

Simplifying ratios

Two families are going for a day trip to Blackpool.

There are 6 people in the Green family and 4 in the Brown family.

They rent a minibus for the day. It costs £60.

How much does each family pay?

There are 10 people altogether.

So each person pays $\frac{£60}{10}$ = £6.

The Green family pays 6 $\times$ £6 = £36
The Brown family pays 4 $\times$ £6 = £24

> Notice that £36 + £24 = £60.
> It works out.

The £60 is split in the **ratio** 36:24.

You can simplify this: Divide by 6 to get 6:4

> This is the ratio of the numbers in the two families

       and further: Divide by 2 to get 3:2

> simplest form

(You could also divide by 12 straight away to get 3:2.)

Ratios are usually written in their simplest whole number form.

In this case, it is 3:2.

Another way to work out the cost is to say

    Greens' share   Browns' share

   $\frac{6}{10} \times £60 = £36$ $\frac{4}{10} \times £60 = £24$

The fractions $\frac{6}{10}$ and $\frac{4}{10}$ are called the **proportions** of the cost that the two families have to pay.

Notice that $\frac{6}{10}$ is $\dfrac{\text{the number of Greens}}{\text{the number of people}}$.

> Greens and Browns together

1 Write each ratio in its simplest form.

a) 6:3   b) 20:100   c) 24:6   d) 10:15

e) 21:7   f) 75:25   g) 12:30   h) 250:400

2 Write each ratio in its simplest form. (You need to put both sides in the same units first.)

a) 20 minutes : 1 hour   b) 1 kilogram : 5 grams

c) 2 cm : 5 mm   d) 80 pence : £2

e) $2\frac{1}{2}$ seconds : 15 seconds   f) 10 hours : $7\frac{1}{2}$ hours

g) 2.4 kg : 6 kg   h) 5.6 kg : 2.1 kg

3 450 grams of brass is made using the metals copper and zinc in the ratio 2:1.

How much of each metal is used?

4 Milton and Spencer share a £60 bonus in the ratio 3:2.

How much do they each get?

5 Ceri and Andrea are business partners who share profits in the ratio 3:5. How much will each get from a profit of £20 000?

6 This bar chart shows the number of employees a company has at three factories.

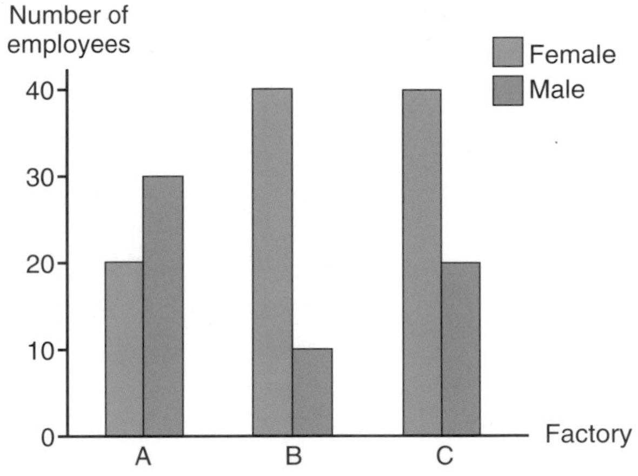

a) What is the ratio of female to male employees at

(i) A? (ii) B? (iii) C?

b) What is the ratio of female to male employees in the company?

c) What fraction of the company's employees are male?

Look at the Nutrition information on a cereal packet. For each item, two figures are given. The first is the amount per 100 g. The second is the amount in a typical serving. Some packets include the milk in the second figure, others do not.

Find an example of each, and in each case explain how the second figure is worked out.

Best buy

Sunil is at the supermarket.

He needs some milk.

Sunil compares the prices by working out the price of 1 pint from each container.

From the 4 pint container: $\frac{100}{4} = 25$

This is £1 in pence

So 1 pint is 25 p.

From the 6 pint container: $\frac{144}{6} = 24$

This is £1.44 in pence

So 1 pint is 24 p.

So this is the better buy

Why doesn't everyone buy this size container?

Sunil wants some breakfast cereal.

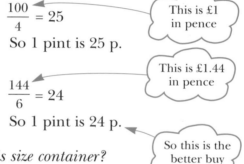

Instead of working out the cost of 1 g of cereal, Sunil notices that 250 g is half of 500 g.

Two 250 g packets cost $2 \times £0.79 = £1.58$.

This is what 500 g costs in small boxes

One 500 g packet costs £1.29.

This is what 500 g costs in a big box

So this is the better buy

Why doesn't Sunil work out the cost of 1 g of cereal?

In questions 1 to 4, which is the better buy?

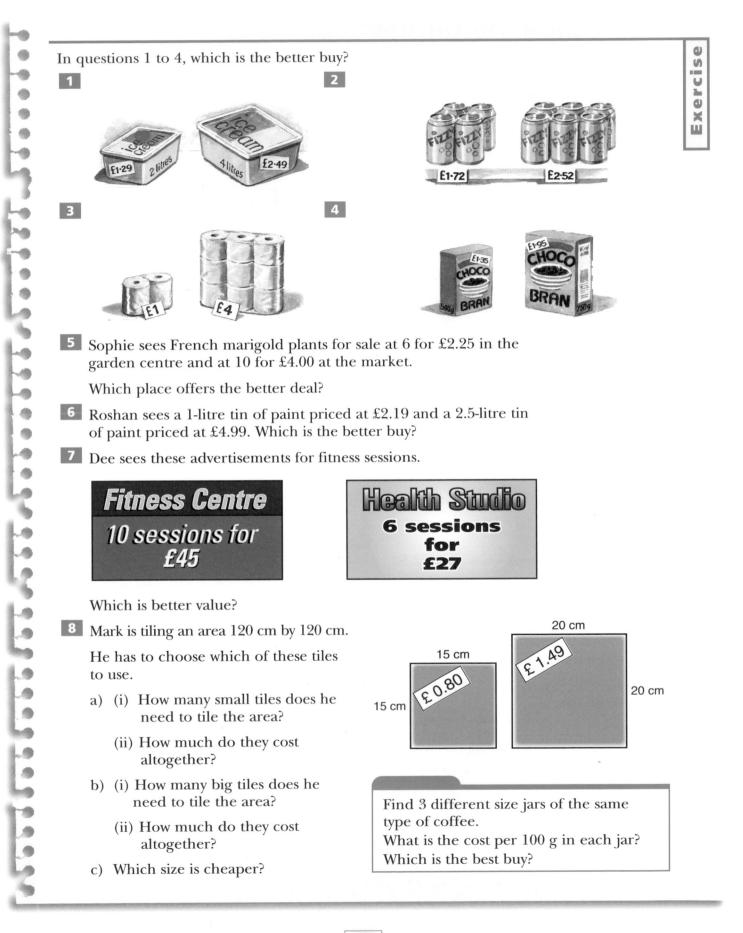

1

£1·29 2 litres   £2·49 4 litres

2

£1·72   £2·52

3

£1   £4

4

£1·35 CHOCO BRAN 500g   £1·95 CHOCO BRAN 750g

5 Sophie sees French marigold plants for sale at 6 for £2.25 in the garden centre and at 10 for £4.00 at the market.

Which place offers the better deal?

6 Roshan sees a 1-litre tin of paint priced at £2.19 and a 2.5-litre tin of paint priced at £4.99. Which is the better buy?

7 Dee sees these advertisements for fitness sessions.

Fitness Centre
10 sessions for £45

Health Studio
6 sessions for £27

Which is better value?

8 Mark is tiling an area 120 cm by 120 cm.

He has to choose which of these tiles to use.

a) (i) How many small tiles does he need to tile the area?

 (ii) How much do they cost altogether?

b) (i) How many big tiles does he need to tile the area?

 (ii) How much do they cost altogether?

c) Which size is cheaper?

15 cm   15 cm   £ 0.80

20 cm   20 cm   £ 1.49

Find 3 different size jars of the same type of coffee.
What is the cost per 100 g in each jar?
Which is the best buy?

Changing money

Each country has its own money.

The UK uses pounds and pence.

What does the USA use?

How do you get foreign money?

Tina is on holiday in New York.

She wants to change £200 into dollars.

> $ means dollars

The bank changes pounds into dollars by multiplying by 1.60.

$$200 \times 1.60 = 320$$

Tina gets $320 for her £200.

How much does she get for £300?

How much for £150?

Tina buys a guide book for $20.

She works out the cost in pounds by dividing by 1.60.

$$20 \div 1.60 = 12.5$$

So the book costs her £12.50.

What is $50 in pounds?

Tina writes down some conversions so that she knows how much she is spending.

£	$
1	1·60
2	3·20
3	4·80
4	
5	8·00
10	16·00
20	32·00
50	
100	

What should the missing entries be?

How can Tina use this to work out $70 in pounds?

Look at these exchange rates.

Use them to answer the questions on this page.

Exchange rates £1=
9 French francs (France)
220 pesetas (Spain)
2.28 Swiss francs (Switzerland)

1 How many French francs do you get for

   a) £1?   b) £10?   c) £60?

2 How many Spanish pesetas do you get for

   a) £1?   b) £5?   c) £25?

3 How many Swiss francs do you get for

   a) £1?   b) £10?   c) £15?

4 Reni is on holiday in Spain.

   a) He buys a meal for 4400 pesetas.

      What is this in pounds?

   b) He spends 500 pesetas on postcards.

      What is this in pounds and pence?

5 Copy and complete this French franc conversion chart.

1F	2F	3F	4F	5F	10F	20F	50F	75F	100F
£0.11	£0.22				£1.11				

6 Paula is in Paris for the weekend.

She wants to buy her sister a present, but can't afford to spend more than £5.

Which of these can she afford?

55F   40F   45F   50F

Exchange rates are changing all the time.

Go to a foreign exchange or look in a newspaper or on Teletext and find out the current exchange rates for Italy, Germany, Portugal, Austria, Greece, Australia, Japan and France.

How much do you get in each of these countries for £100?

Exercise

Finishing off

Now that you have finished this chapter you should be able to

- ★ write a ratio as a fraction, decimal or percentage
- ★ write a ratio in its simplest form
- ★ solve simple problems using ratio
- ★ compare prices and work out the 'best buy'
- ★ change money.

Use the questions in the next exercise to check that you understand everything.

Mixed exercise

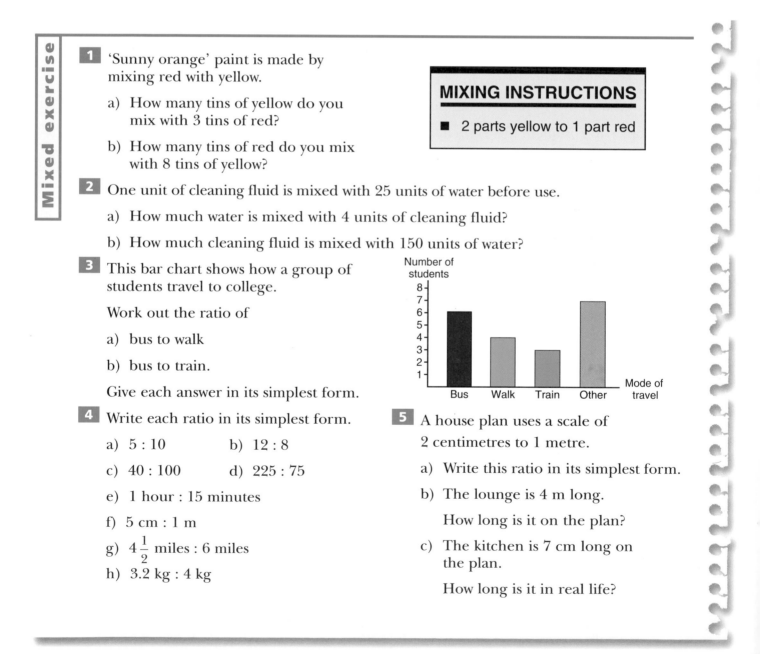

1 'Sunny orange' paint is made by mixing red with yellow.

a) How many tins of yellow do you mix with 3 tins of red?

b) How many tins of red do you mix with 8 tins of yellow?

MIXING INSTRUCTIONS

■ 2 parts yellow to 1 part red

2 One unit of cleaning fluid is mixed with 25 units of water before use.

a) How much water is mixed with 4 units of cleaning fluid?

b) How much cleaning fluid is mixed with 150 units of water?

3 This bar chart shows how a group of students travel to college.

Work out the ratio of

a) bus to walk

b) bus to train.

Give each answer in its simplest form.

Number of students

(bar chart: Bus 6, Walk 4, Train 3, Other 7)

Mode of travel

4 Write each ratio in its simplest form.

a) 5 : 10   b) 12 : 8

c) 40 : 100   d) 225 : 75

e) 1 hour : 15 minutes

f) 5 cm : 1 m

g) $4\frac{1}{2}$ miles : 6 miles

h) 3.2 kg : 4 kg

5 A house plan uses a scale of 2 centimetres to 1 metre.

a) Write this ratio in its simplest form.

b) The lounge is 4 m long.

   How long is it on the plan?

c) The kitchen is 7 cm long on the plan.

   How long is it in real life?

6 Helen and Clare share a house.

a) The rent is £100 and they pay it in the ratio 2:3.

How much does each of them pay?

b) The phone bill is £140 and they pay it in the ratio 5:2.

How much does each of them pay?

7 For each of these items work out which is the better buy.

a)

£1.05   £1.59   Margarine 500 g   Margarine 750 g

b)

60 Vitamin Tablets £2.79   120 Vitamin Tablets £5.25

c)

5 Kg Potatoes £3   10 Kg Potatoes £5

8 Nicky wants to learn to drive.

She sees these adverts.

MOTOR SCHOOL

12 lessons for £150

Learn to drive

9 lessons for £120

10th lesson free

How much does one lesson cost at each school?

9 Kerry and Liam are on holiday in the USA.

The exchange rate is £1 = $1.60.

a) How many dollars does Liam get for £80?

b) How many dollars does Kerry get for £140?

c) Liam pays $20 for a coach ticket.

How much is this in pounds and pence?

d) Kerry pays $110 for a hotel room.

How much is this to the nearest pound?

Describe 4 ways in which you have used ratio and proportion in other subjects.

Fourteen

Area and volume

Before you start this chapter you should

★ be able to find the perimeter of a shape with straight sides

★ remember that area is measured in square units like cm^2 or m^2 and volume is measured in cubic units like cm^3 or m^3

★ be able to find or estimate the area of a shape drawn on a grid of squares

★ be able to find the area of a rectangle

★ be able to find the area of a shape made from rectangles

★ be able to find the volume of a cuboid by counting cubes.

Use the following questions to check that you still remember these topics.

Reminder

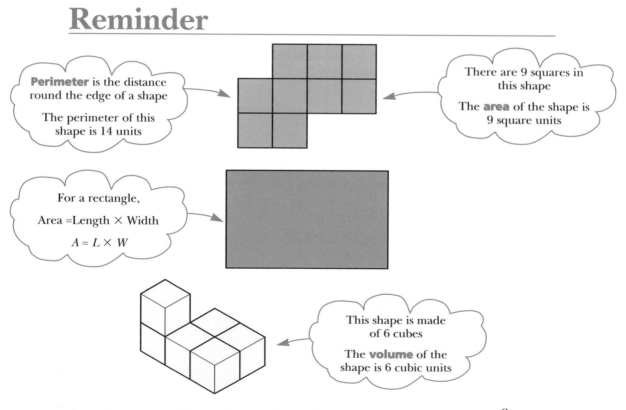

Perimeter is the distance round the edge of a shape

The perimeter of this shape is 14 units

There are 9 squares in this shape

The **area** of the shape is 9 square units

For a rectangle,

Area =Length × Width

$A = L \times W$

This shape is made of 6 cubes

The **volume** of the shape is 6 cubic units

Area is measured in square units such as square centimetres (cm^2) and square metres (m^2).

Volume is measured in cubic units such as cubic centimetres (cm^3) and cubic metres (m^3).

1 Find the perimeter and area of these shapes.

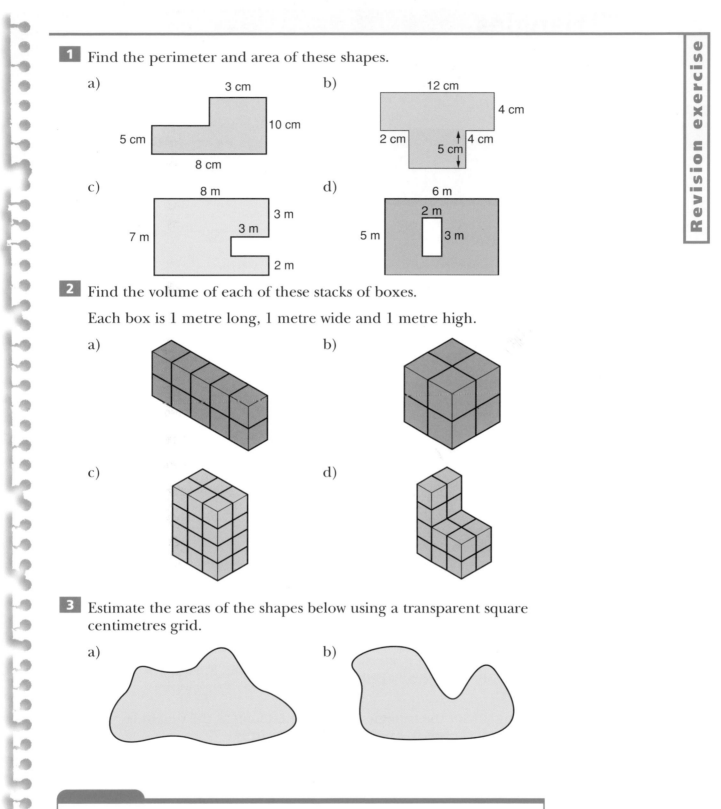

a)

3 cm

10 cm

5 cm

8 cm

b)

12 cm

4 cm

2 cm   4 cm

5 cm

c)

8 m

3 m

3 m

7 m

2 m

d)

6 m

2 m

5 m   3 m

2 Find the volume of each of these stacks of boxes.

Each box is 1 metre long, 1 metre wide and 1 metre high.

a)

b)

c)

d)

3 Estimate the areas of the shapes below using a transparent square centimetres grid.

a)

b)

Make a suitable grid and use it to estimate an area on a real map, like you did in question 3. It can be a map of an island, a county, a town or anything else you can get a map of.

Triangles

Jenille and Imran are taking part in a kite-making competition.

Jenille cuts out 2 right angled triangles from a rectangular piece of material for his kite.

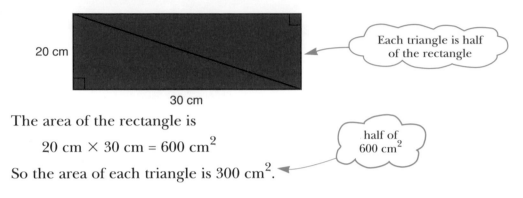

> Each triangle is half of the rectangle

The area of the rectangle is

$$20 \text{ cm} \times 30 \text{ cm} = 600 \text{ cm}^2$$

> half of 600 cm^2

So the area of each triangle is 300 cm^2.

Imran decides to make his kite from two triangles joined together as well.

Even though he does not use a right angled triangle, it is still half a rectangle.

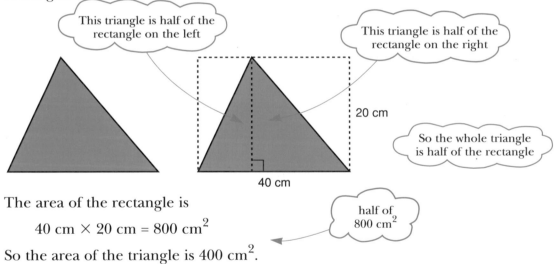

> This triangle is half of the rectangle on the left

> This triangle is half of the rectangle on the right

> So the whole triangle is half of the rectangle

The area of the rectangle is

$$40 \text{ cm} \times 20 \text{ cm} = 800 \text{ cm}^2$$

> half of 800 cm^2

So the area of the triangle is 400 cm^2.

To find the area of any triangle, you multiply the base by the height and halve the answer.

You can use any side of the triangle as the base, as long as the height is at right angles to it. This is the **perpendicular height**

Area of a triangle = $\frac{1}{2}$ × Base × Perpendicular Height

$$A = \frac{1}{2} \times B \times H$$

How do you think Jenille and Imran will join the triangles together to make kite shapes?

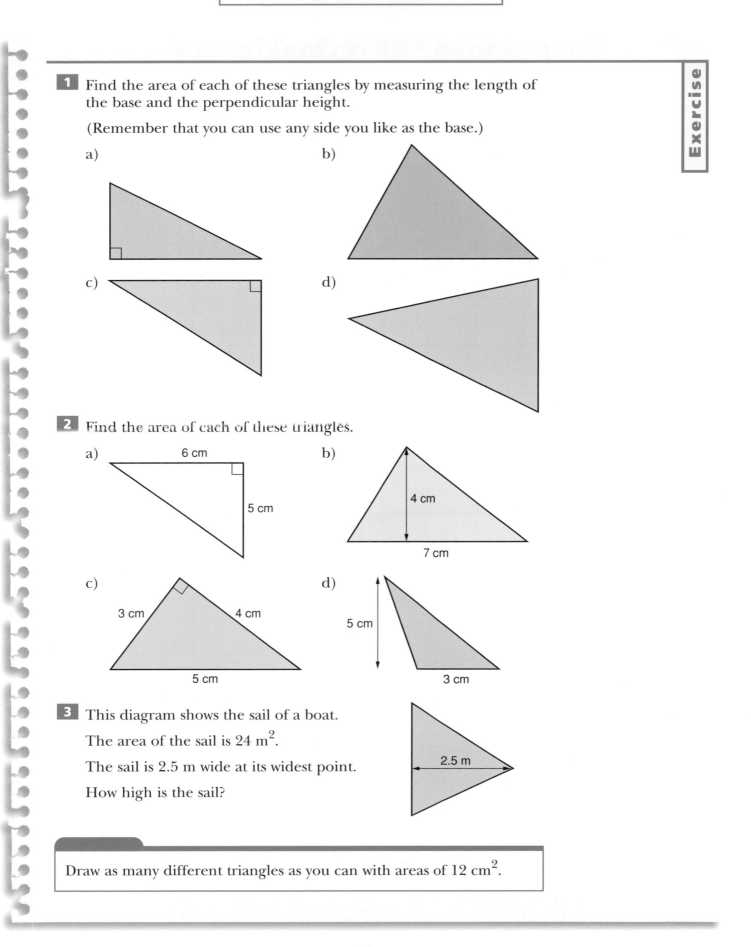

1 Find the area of each of these triangles by measuring the length of the base and the perpendicular height.

(Remember that you can use any side you like as the base.)

a)

b)

c)

d)

2 Find the area of each of these triangles.

a) 6 cm
5 cm

b) 4 cm
7 cm

c) 3 cm 4 cm
5 cm

d) 5 cm
3 cm

3 This diagram shows the sail of a boat.

The area of the sail is 24 m².

The sail is 2.5 m wide at its widest point.

How high is the sail?

2.5 m

Draw as many different triangles as you can with areas of 12 cm².

Shapes made of rectangles and triangles

How would you work out the area of this field?

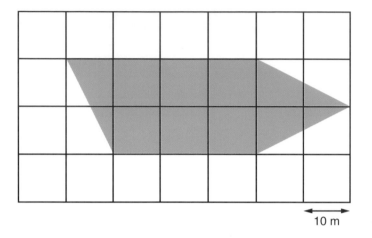

10 m

At first glance it looks like quite a complicated shape.

But it can easily be split up into simpler shapes – a rectangle and two triangles.

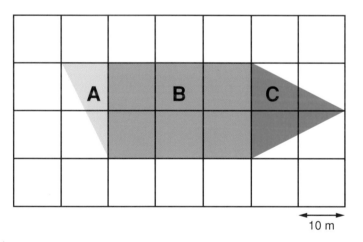

10 m

You can work out the area by finding the area of the simple shapes and adding them together.

Area of triangle A = $\frac{1}{2} \times$ 10 m $\times$ 20 m = 100 m^2

Area of rectangle B = 20 m $\times$ 30 m = 600 m^2

Area of triangle C = $\frac{1}{2} \times$ 20 m $\times$ 20 m = 200 m^2

So the area of the field = 100 m^2 + 600 m^2 + 200 m^2
= 900 m^2

Do you think a real field would fit exactly in the grid like this one?

1 Find the area of each of these fields by splitting them up into rectangles and triangles.

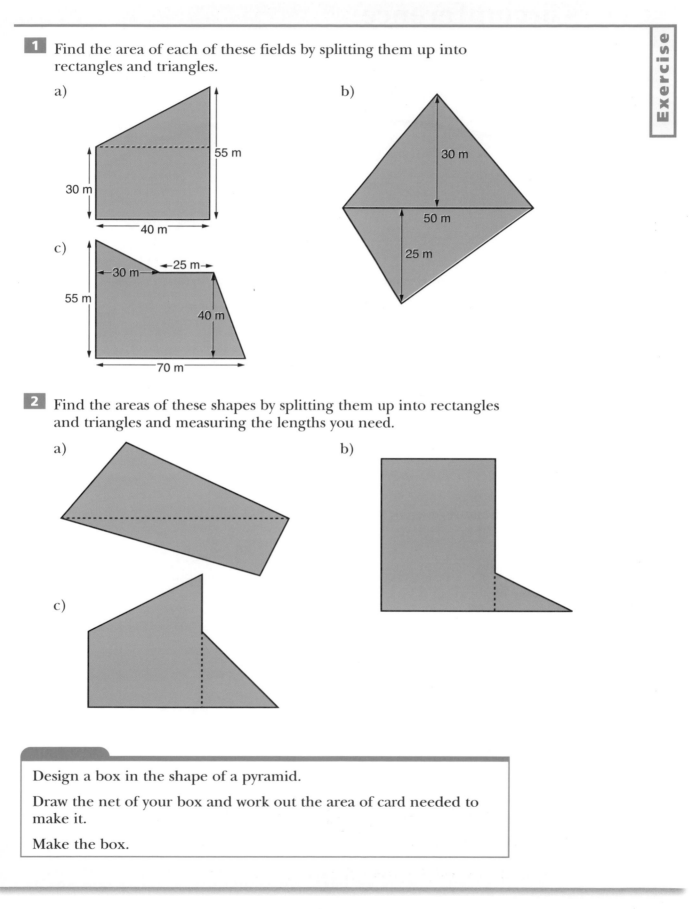

a)

55 m

30 m

40 m

b)

30 m

50 m

25 m

c)

25 m

30 m

55 m

40 m

70 m

2 Find the areas of these shapes by splitting them up into rectangles and triangles and measuring the lengths you need.

a)

b)

c)

Design a box in the shape of a pyramid.

Draw the net of your box and work out the area of card needed to make it.

Make the box.

Circumference

Harry is walking around a circular lake in his local park.

He knows that the diameter is 50 m and wonders how far it is all the way round. (He does not have much time.)

The distance around the edge of a circle is called the **circumference**

The circumference can be found by multiplying the diameter by a number called pi, which is written π.

> The value of π is about 3.14. Your calculator may have a button for π, if not you can use 3.14

> Also, $C = 2\pi r$ where r is the radius

Circumference of a circle = π × diameter

$$C = \pi \times d$$

So the circumference of the lake is
π × 50 m = 157 m

If you know the circumference of a circle, you can work out the diameter by dividing it by π.

Example

The circumference of the Earth is about 40 000 km.

What is its radius?

Solution

> The radius is half the diameter

Circumference = π × diameter

> Divide this by π

40 000 = π × diameter

12732 = diameter

radius = 12732 ÷ 2

So the radius of the Earth is about 6366 km.

1 Find the circumferences of the following circles. If you do not have a π button on your calculator, use the value 3.14 for π.

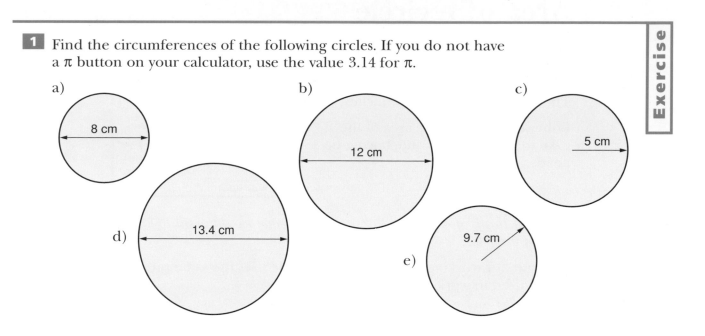

a)

8 cm

b)

12 cm

c)

5 cm

d)

13.4 cm

e)

9.7 cm

2 Find the diameters of the circles with the following circumferences:

a) Circumference = 20 cm

b) Circumference = 42 cm

c) Circumference = 17 cm

3 A bicycle wheel has a diameter of 70 cm.

a) How far does the bicycle travel in the time it takes for the wheel to go round once?

b) How many times does the wheel go round in the time it takes for the cyclist to travel 1 kilometre?

70 cm

Measure the diameters of three different bicycle wheels.

Work out how many times the wheels go round in one kilometre.

Do you prefer to ride a bicycle with big wheels or small wheels? Give some reasons.

Area of a circle

Bob works in a cake factory.

He has designed a new birthday cake.

The radius of the cake is 6 inches.

Bob wants to know the area of the cake to work out how much icing he needs.

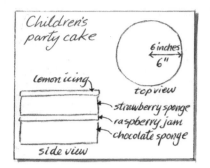

 Can you think of any other cases where someone would want to know the area of a circle?

The rule for working out the area of a circle uses the same number, π, that is used to work out the circumference.

$$\textbf{Area of a circle} = \pi r^2$$

$$A = \pi r^2$$

r stands for the radius

For Bob's new cake,

$$Area = \pi r^2$$
$$= \pi \times 6^2$$
$$= \pi \times 36$$
$$= 113 \text{ square inches}$$

You only square the radius. You work it out by squaring the radius first, then multiplying by π

Finding the radius from the area

When you know the area and want to know the radius, you need to work backwards.

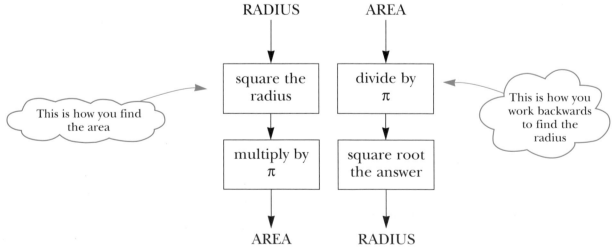

This is how you find the area

This is how you work backwards to find the radius

 How can you work out the area if you only know the diameter?

1 Work out the areas of these circles:

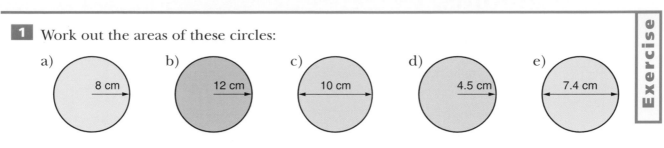

a)
8 cm

b)
12 cm

c)
10 cm

d)
4.5 cm

e)
7.4 cm

2 Work out the radius of circles with these areas:

a) Area = 20 cm^2 b) Area = 38 cm^2 c) Area = 11 cm^2

3 The diagram shows an arched window made from a rectangle with half a circle above it.

Find the area of glass needed for the window.

2 m

3 m

4 This garden pond has an island in the middle of it.

The diameter of the island is 1 m.

The diameter of the pond is 5 m.

Find the area of pond that contains water.

5 Julie is making circular badges out of card.

Each badge has a diameter of 7 cm.

She is using a piece of A4 card which measures 29.7 cm by 21.0 cm.

a) How many badges will Julie be able to fit on the piece of card?

b) Find the area of one badge.

c) Work out the area of card that will be wasted.

6 Sanjay wants a circular flower bed in his garden.

He has enough plants to fill an area of 10 m^2.

What is the radius of the biggest flower bed he can have?

Look at the different sizes of pizza in a supermarket or restaurant.

Work out the area of each pizza.

Do you think the prices are fair?

Cuboids

The diagram shows a small box of cereal.

How much room is there in the box?

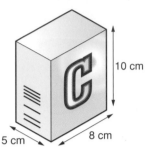

10 cm

5 cm   8 cm

The amount of space taken up by the box is called the **volume.**

It is measured in cubic units. The volume of the box of cereal is measured in cubic centimetres (cm^3).

To find the volume of the box, you need to know how many cubic centimetres it takes up.

So imagine you have a lot of cubes, 1 cm long, 1 cm wide and 1 cm high.

Each cube has a volume of 1 cm^3.

You are finding out how many of these cubes fit in the box.

The bottom of the box is a rectangle 8 cm long and 5 cm wide.
$8 \times 5 = 40$

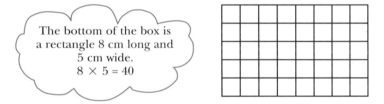

So 40 cubes can be fitted in the bottom of the box.

The box is 10 cm high.
Each layer has 40 cubes.
There are 10 layers.
$40 \times 10 = 400$

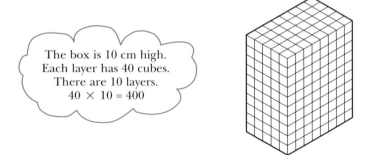

There are 400 cubes altogether. So the box has a volume of 400 cm^3.

The number of cubes in the bottom of the box was found by multiplying the length by the width. To find the total number of cubes in the box, this was then multiplied by the height of the box.

Volume of a cuboid = Length $\times$ Width $\times$ Height

$$V = L \times W \times H$$

Check that this formula works.

What happens if you turn the box on its side?

1 Find the volume of each of the following cuboids.

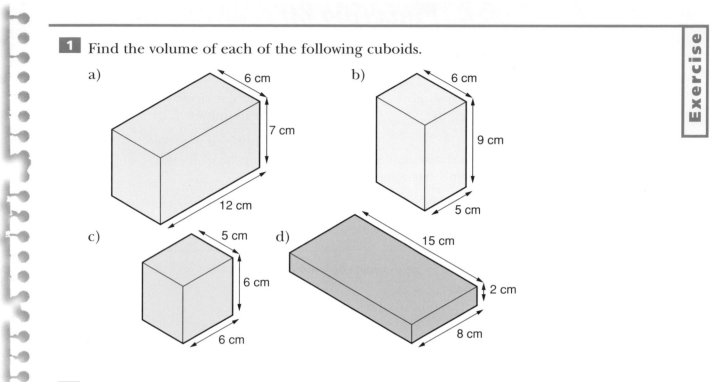

a) 6 cm, 7 cm, 12 cm

b) 6 cm, 9 cm, 5 cm

c) 5 cm, 6 cm, 6 cm

d) 15 cm, 2 cm, 8 cm

2 A fish tank is 60 cm long and 40 cm wide.

It is filled with water to a depth of 30 cm.

Find the volume of water in the tank.

3 A box containing 350 cm^3 of icing sugar is 7 cm long and 4 cm wide.

What depth of icing sugar is in the box?

4 An open topped box is made by cutting out a rectangle 15 cm by 12 cm, and cutting a square 3 cm by 3 cm off each corner.

Find the volume of the box.

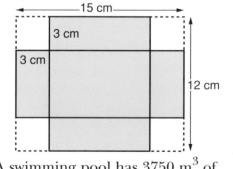

15 cm, 3 cm, 3 cm, 12 cm

5 A swimming pool has 3750 m^3 of water in it.

It is 3 metres deep, and the length of the pool is twice its width.

Find the length of the pool.

Look at packets of your favourite cereal in the supermarket.

Work out the volume of the different sized packets it comes in.

Do you think the prices are fair?

Finishing off

> **Now that you have finished this chapter you should be able to**
>
> ★ find the area of a triangle from base and height measurements
>
> ★ find the area of a shape made up of rectangles and triangles
>
> ★ find the circumference of a circle from its radius or diameter
>
> ★ find the area of a circle from its radius or diameter
>
> ★ find the volume of a cuboid from the lengths of its sides.

Use the questions in the next exercise to check that you understand everything.

Mixed exercise

1 Find the area of each of these shapes.

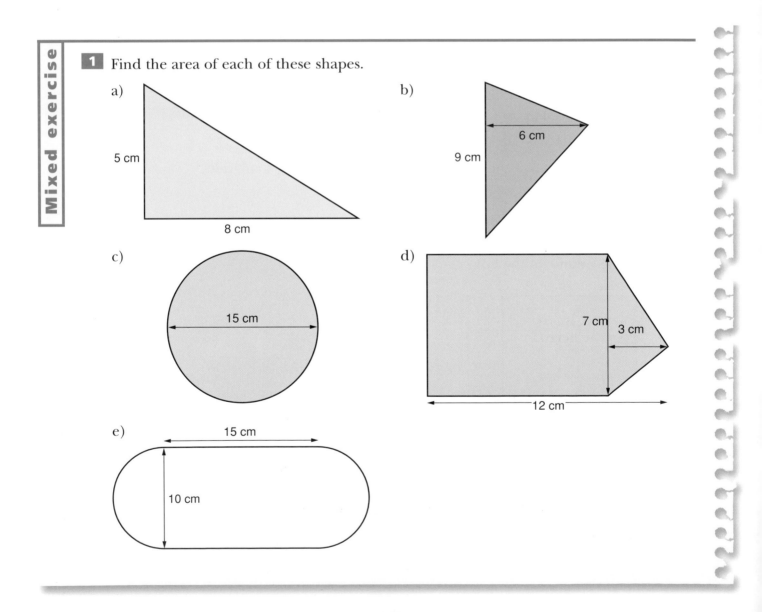

a)

5 cm

8 cm

b)

6 cm

9 cm

c)

15 cm

d)

7 cm   3 cm

12 cm

e)

15 cm

10 cm

2 A circular pond has a diameter of 4 metres. It is surrounded by a path 80 cm (0.8 m) wide.

a) Find the circumference of the pond.

b) Find the area of the pond.

c) Find the area of the path. (Hint: find the area of the larger circle first.)

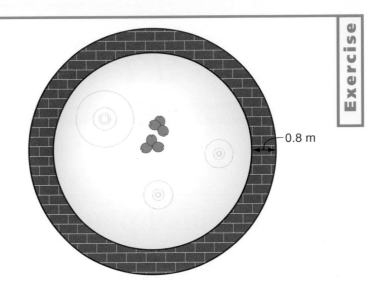

0.8 m

3 Find the volume of each of these boxes.

a)

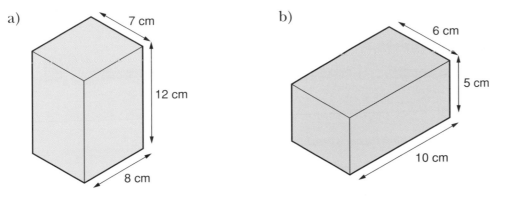

7 cm

12 cm

8 cm

b)

6 cm

5 cm

10 cm

4 A box of cereal is 20 cm long, 8 cm wide and 30 cm high.

a) Find the volume of the box.

b) Another box is to be made which has $\frac{3}{4}$ of the volume of the first one. It is to be 18 cm long and 8 cm wide. Find the height of the second box.

Draw a circle, with a radius of a whole number of millimetres between 20 mm and 80 mm, on 1 mm square graph paper. Find the area of the circle by counting squares. (You can make this easier by drawing large squares and rectangles inside the circle and then counting the leftover 1 mm squares on the edge.)

Use the area you have found to calculate an estimate for π.

Compare your answer with the rest of the class.

Fifteen

Approximations

Before you start this chapter you should be able to

★ round to the nearest whole number

★ round to the nearest ten, hundred and so on.

Decimal places

Shock school survey!
A survey of 21 classrooms found a staggering 746 pupils.
That's an average 35.5238 pupils per class!

What does '35.5238 pupils' mean?

Do you think the newspaper should use 4 decimal places here?

How many decimal places would you use?

Look at this number line from 35.4 to 35.6.

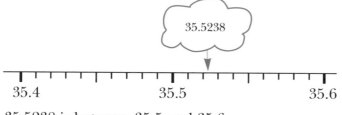

35.5238 is between 35.5 and 35.6.

It is nearer to 35.5.

So 35.5238 to 1 decimal place is 35.5.

What is it to 2 decimal places?

What is it to the nearest whole number?

What about numbers like 14.65?

Usually you round up with 5s, so 14.65 to 1 decimal place is 14.7.

A calculation like £7.64 ÷ 5 gives £1.528. This is rounded to the nearest penny (which is the same as rounding it to two decimal places) to get £1.53.

1 Write these numbers to 1 decimal place.

a) 1.59   b) 3.812   c) 6.15

d) 2.66   e) 55.239   f) 14.745

2 Write these numbers to 2 decimal places.

a) 3.581   b) 17.612   c) 2.805

d) 10.478   e) 6.333   f) 0.3957

3 How many decimal places do you give if your answer is correct to the nearest

a) tenth?

b) hundredth?

4

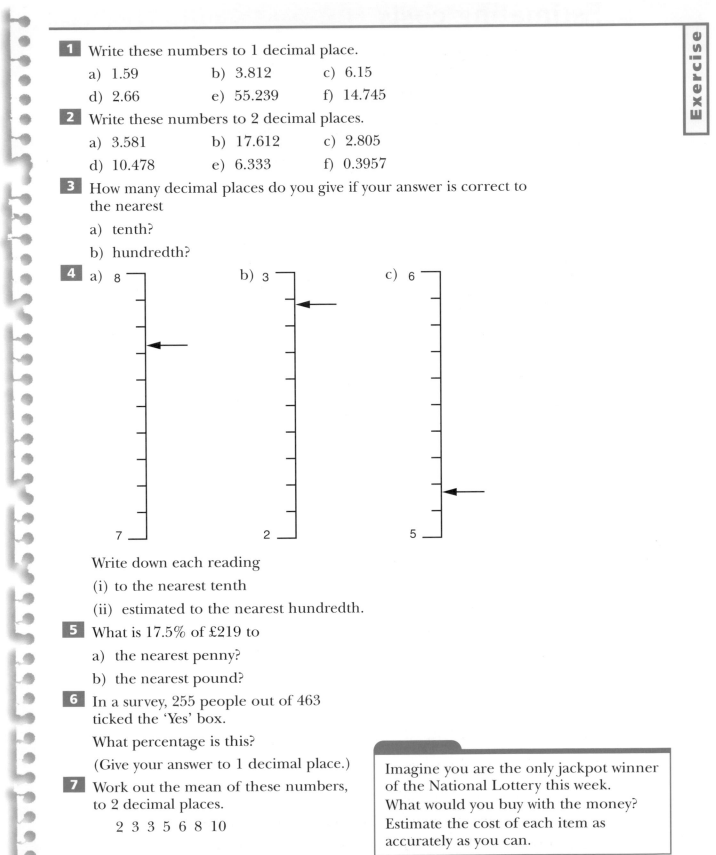

a) 8 ... 7

b) 3 ... 2

c) 6 ... 5

Write down each reading

(i) to the nearest tenth

(ii) estimated to the nearest hundredth.

5 What is 17.5% of £219 to

a) the nearest penny?

b) the nearest pound?

6 In a survey, 255 people out of 463 ticked the 'Yes' box.

What percentage is this?

(Give your answer to 1 decimal place.)

7 Work out the mean of these numbers, to 2 decimal places.

     2 3 3 5 6 8 10

Imagine you are the only jackpot winner of the National Lottery this week.
What would you buy with the money?
Estimate the cost of each item as accurately as you can.

Estimating costs

Ryan buys these things for his new flat.

Ryan wants to estimate the total cost to check that his bill is 'about right'.

 What is the cost of each item to the nearest pound?

Ryan estimates the total cost by adding these together.

£8 + £8 + £12 = £28

 Work out the exact total of the bill.

A better estimate can be found like this:

£8.49 is about £8.50

£8 + £8.50 + £12 = £28.50

It doesn't really matter that the two estimates differ by 50p.

After all, they are only estimates!

Ryan chooses these tiles for his bathroom.

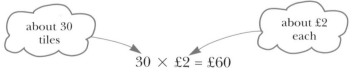

They cost £2.15 each.

Ryan wants to estimate the cost.

 How many tiles are there?

How much is each tile to the nearest pound?

One way to estimate the cost is like this:

about 30 tiles   about £2 each

30 × £2 = £60

 What is the exact cost?

Approximations

1 Estimate the cost of each person's bill.

a) Emil buys 8 rolls of wallpaper.

b) Lee buys 2 tins of paint and a roller.

c) Chloe buys 60 ceiling tiles and a shelf kit.

d) Dean buys a paint brush and 3 tins of paint.

e) Kashmir buys 6 rolls of wallpaper and 80 ceiling tiles.

f) Lisa buys 2 rollers, a paint brush and 4 tins of paint.

2 Alan is a student.

His rent is £59.85 a week.

Three bills have just arrived. They are

Estimate how much Alan has to pay on rent, gas, electricity and water in a year.

Estimate the cost of a weekend away at a youth hostel.

Rough calculations

Aisha is a builder. Her next job is to build this wall.

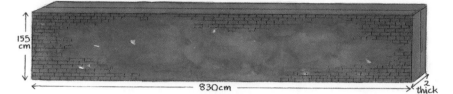

She needs to know about how many bricks to order for the job.

Each brick looks like this:

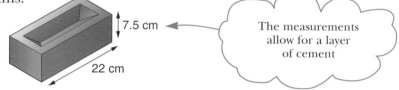

The measurements allow for a layer of cement

Aisha estimates how many bricks fit along the wall.

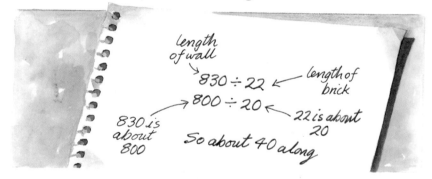

length of wall
$830 \div 22$ ← length of brick
$800 \div 20$ ← 22 is about 20
830 is about 800
So about 40 along

There are about 40 bricks along the wall.

Now she estimates the number of layers.

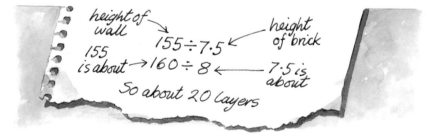

height of wall
$155 \div 7.5$ ← height of brick
155 is about → $160 \div 8$ ← 7.5 is about
So about 20 layers

There are about 20 layers of bricks.

So, altogether, she needs about

$$40 \times 20 \times 2$$

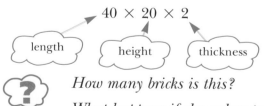

length   height   thickness

How many bricks is this?

What happens if she orders too many?

What happens if she orders too few?

How many should she order?

1 Mick, Rajit, Julie and Kath are all going to Leeds for a party at Sue's house.

This map shows the distances between their home towns.

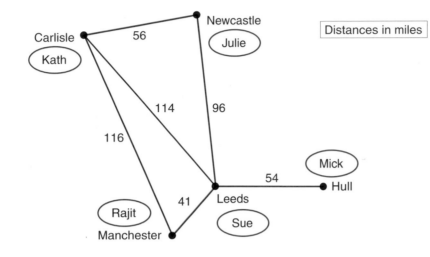

Distances in miles

a) Estimate how far each person has to travel by writing distances to the nearest 10 miles.

b) Do you think the distances on the map are exact?

2 A field is being used as a car park. It is nearly full.

Arthur counts 12 rows of cars and 52 cars in one of the rows.

Estimate the number of cars in the field.

3 Wesley is tiling part of his bathroom wall.

The area he is tiling is 187 cm long and 106 cm high.

The tiles are 10 cm × 10 cm.

Estimate the number of tiles

a) along the length

b) down the height

c) altogether.

4 This piece of land is sold for building.

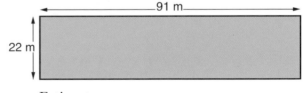

Estimate

a) the area of the land

b) how many plots 9 m wide and 22 m long the area can be divided into

c) the area of each plot.

Estimate how many badminton courts can fit on to a 5-a-side pitch.

Rough checks for your calculator

Add up these numbers on your calculator:

$$
\begin{array}{r}
381 \\
1027 \\
602 \\
+\ 478 \\
\hline
\end{array}
$$

 How do you know that your calculator gets it right? (Maybe you pressed the wrong buttons!)

A good way to check that the calculator is 'about right' is to approximate each number first, and then add them up.

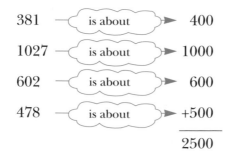

381	is about	400
1027	is about	1000
602	is about	600
478	is about	+500
		2500

 Is 2500 about the same as your calculator gets?

Where do you use calculations like this?

Now work out this multiplication on your calculator:

$$185 \times 107 \times 379$$

Again, you can check that the answer is 'about right' by approximating each number, like this:

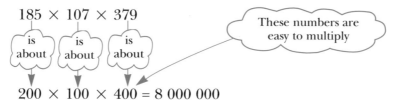

$$185 \times 107 \times 379$$

is about   is about   is about

These numbers are easy to multiply

$$200 \times 100 \times 400 = 8\ 000\ 000$$

 Is 8 000 000 about the same as your calculator gets?

Where do you use calculations like this?

The next problem is a bit harder.

$$\frac{61+77+84+69+12+28+99+10+42}{9}$$

 Work out the answer on your calculator.

Now approximate each number and check that the answer is 'about right'. (Hint: what is each number to the nearest ten?)

Where do you use calculations like this?

Approximations

1 Work out each of these on your calculator, and then approximate the numbers to check that you are 'about right'.

a) 68
    11
    +22
    ——

b) 13 × 81 × 21

c) 104
    213
    +689
    ——

2 This is Louise's supermarket receipt.

```
............ 1.21
............ 0.89
............ 0.92
............ 2.03
............ 1.79
............ 1.12
............ 2.68
··························
      10.64
— Please call again —
```

Check that the total is 'about right' by writing each item to the nearest pound and then adding.

3 Estimate, to the nearest pound, the admission cost of

a) 1 adult

b) 1 child

c) 2 adults and 3 children.

Admission

Adults £3.90
Children ½ price

4 Find a rough answer for each of these calculations:

a) 4.8 + 7.1   b) 9.1 − 6.9   c) 4.1 × 2.9

d) 51% of 203   e) 24% of 97   f) 48% of 59

5 5971 people live in Hilltop. 24.4% of them are younger than 16.

a) How many people, to the nearest thousand, live in Hilltop?

b) How many of them, to the nearest hundred, are younger than 16?

Measure a sardine tin and so estimate its volume.

Use your answer to estimate the volume of a sardine.

Finishing off

> **Now that you have finished this chapter you should be able to**
>
> ★ round to a given number of decimal places
>
> ★ estimate costs
>
> ★ make rough calculations
>
> ★ do rough checks for your calculator.

Use the questions in the next exercise to check that you understand everything.

Mixed exercise

1 Use your calculator to find the square root of 13.

Write it correct to

a) 1 decimal place   b) 2 decimal places   c) 3 decimal places.

2

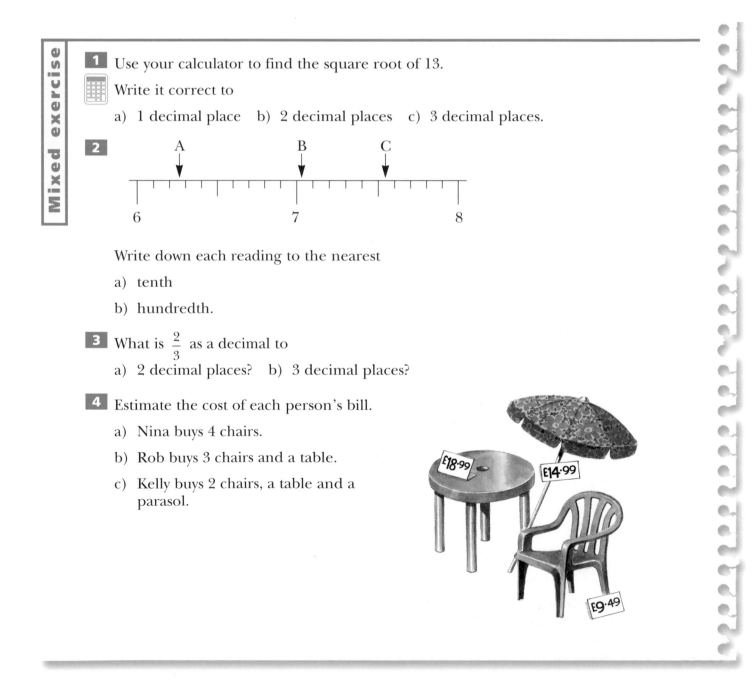

Write down each reading to the nearest

a) tenth

b) hundredth.

3 What is $\frac{2}{3}$ as a decimal to

a) 2 decimal places?   b) 3 decimal places?

4 Estimate the cost of each person's bill.

a) Nina buys 4 chairs.

b) Rob buys 3 chairs and a table.

c) Kelly buys 2 chairs, a table and a parasol.

£18·99   £14·99   £9·49

5 A football team plays 21 home games in a season.

604 519 people go to watch in total.

Estimate the number of people at each game.

6 A playground is 48 m by 31 m.

a) Round each number to the nearest ten.

b) Estimate the area of the playground.

7 Bianca drives 154 miles from London to Cardiff for a business meeting. She thinks she does an average of 50–55 miles an hour.

Estimate how long she takes.

8 Give a rough answer for each of these calculations:

a) $\frac{1}{2}$ of 99   b) $\frac{3}{4}$ of 82   c) $\frac{1}{3}$ of 589

d) $5.1 + 7.89$ e) 8.12×4.93 f) $30.3 \div 5.2$

g) 49% of 151   h) 76% of 205

9 Estimate how much this bike costs in the sale.

10 Peter's car does 38 miles per gallon.

a) Write this number to the nearest 10.

He drives 158.7 miles.

b) Write this number to the nearest 10.

c) Estimate how many gallons of petrol Peter used.

11 In a survey, 980 teenagers are asked about their New Year's resolutions.

10% want to stop smoking.

24% want to eat less chocolate.

51% want to do more exercise.

Estimate the number of teenagers in each of these groups.

Estimate the cost of buying and running a car.

Sixteen

Probability

Use the following questions to check that you still remember these topics.

Revision exercise

1 a) Write down the probability that:

  (i) when a coin is tossed it comes up heads

  (ii) when a die is thrown the number on it is more than 2

  (iii) someone chosen at random was born on a Thursday

  (iv) a card chosen at random from an ordinary pack is a heart

  (v) when a die is thrown the number on it is 7.

 b) Draw a probability scale and mark your answers (i) to (v) on it.

2 A scientist is studying the courtship habits of a type of spider.

She sees 35 occasions when the female kills and eats the male and 15 occasions when the male survives the meeting.

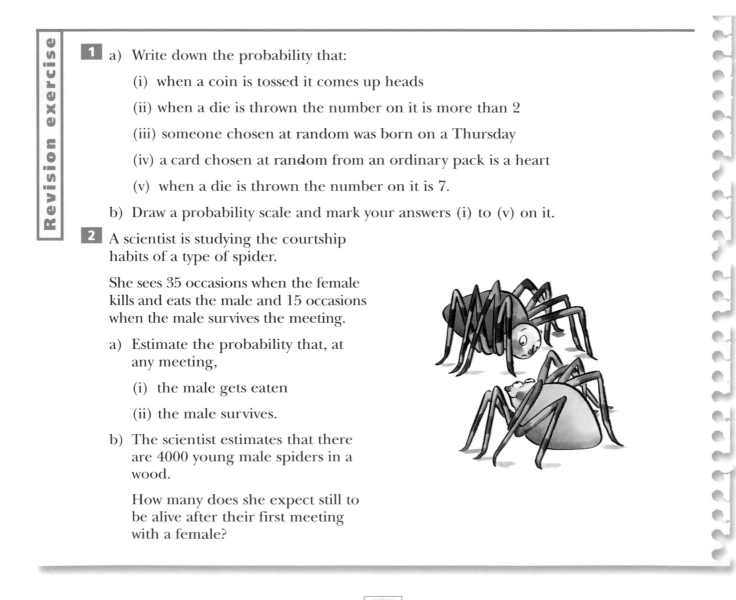

 a) Estimate the probability that, at any meeting,

  (i) the male gets eaten

  (ii) the male survives.

 b) The scientist estimates that there are 4000 young male spiders in a wood.

 How many does she expect still to be alive after their first meeting with a female?

3 In a raffle 250 tickets are sold.

One ticket wins the star prize.

Sanjiv buys 5 tickets.

a) What is the probability that Sanjiv wins the star prize?

b) What is the probability that Sanjiv does not win the star prize?

The draw is made and Sanjiv does not win the star prize.

However, the winner cannot be found and so another ticket is drawn.

c) What is the probability that Sanjiv wins the star prize this time?

4 Alex and Val are playing snap.

Alex chooses the first card; it is the 10 of diamonds. Then Val chooses a card from the same pack.

a) Find the probability that Val's card is:

   (i) another 10 (snap)

   (ii) a higher value card (Ace, King, Queen, Jack)

   (iii) a lower value card.

b) Add your answers to parts (i), (ii) and (iii) together. What do you notice?

5 A doctor finds that out of 80 people who caught a rare disease, 30 died.

a) Estimate the probability that someone catching the disease

   (i) dies

   (ii) does not die.

b) There is a new outbreak of the disease and 60 people catch it. The doctor gives them a new medicine and 54 do not die.

Do you think the new medicine works?

Keep a record each day for one month of whether it is raining when you leave home in the morning. Estimate the probability that it will be raining on any morning.

Repeat the experiment at a different time of year. Are your answers different?

Two events

You are playing Monopoly and are on the square marked GO.

You throw two dice. One is red, the other green.

What is the probability that you score 10 and so land on the square marked JAIL?

Look at the diagram below. It shows different totals for all the ways the dice can land.

	Red die	1	2	3	4	5	6
	1	2	3	4	5	6	7
	2	3	4	5	6	7	8
Green die	3	4	5	6	7	8	9
	4	5	6	7	8	9	10
	5	6	7	8	9	10	11
	6	7	8	9	10	11	12

There are 36 entries in the table.

They are all equally likely.

So each has a probability of $\frac{1}{36}$.

There are three 10s (marked in dark blue).

So the probability of a 10 is $\frac{3}{36}$ or $\frac{1}{12}$.

 What are the probabilities of the other possible totals: 2, 3, 4, . . .9, 11, 12?

Check that the probabilities all add up to 1.

Does it make any difference if both the dice are the same colour?

Another way to tackle this question is to make a list of all the possible outcomes.

$1 + 1 = 2$

$1 + 2 = 3$

$1 + 3 = 4$

. . .

$6 + 6 = 12$

 How many lines does the list have?

Which way is neater, this way or using the table?

1 You have a 10p coin and a 50p coin. You toss both of them.

a) Copy and complete this diagram showing the possible outcomes.

		50p coin	
		Head	**Tail**
10p coin	**Head**	HH	....
	Tail	....	....

b) Write down the probability of

   (i) 2 heads

   (ii) 1 head and 1 tail

   (iii) 2 tails.

c) Show that your three answers to part b) add up to 1.

d) Does it make any difference if both the coins are 50p?

e) Copy and complete this list of the possible outcomes:

HH
...
...
...

3 In a game, a player throws 2 dice. The larger score is taken.

So 3 and 4 scores 4; double 2 scores 2.

a) Make a table showing all the possible scores, like the one on the opposite page.

b) Find the probabilities of all the possible scores.

c) Show that your answers to part b) add up to 1.

2 In the game Ching, Chang, Pok, two players both make a sign with one hand at the same time. It is Paper, Scissors or Stone.

If both players do the same it is a draw.

Otherwise: Paper beats Stone; Stone beats Scissors; Scissors beats Paper.

a) Copy and complete this diagram showing who wins the game when Amelia and Zoe play.

		Amelia		
		Paper	**Stone**	**Scissors**
	Paper	Draw	Z	
Zoe	**Stone**	A		
	Scissors			

b) Amelia and Zoe choose between Paper, Stone and Scissors at random. Find the probability that in any game

   (i) Amelia wins

   (ii) Zoe wins

   (iii) it is a draw.

c) Add your answers to part b) together.

   What do you get?

If you are good at Ching, Chang, Pok (see question 2), you can outguess your opponent and so the probability of your winning is greater. Test your skill by playing a lot of games with a friend.

Record the results and work out the probability of your winning any game.

Finishing off

Use the questions in the next exercise to check that you understand everything.

Mixed exercise

1 A bank card has a 4 digit code number.

This can be any number between 0000 and 9999.

A thief steals a bank card but does not know the code number.

a) The thief tries to use the card by choosing a 4-digit number at random. What is the probability that the number is correct?

b) What is the probability it is wrong?

c) The thief's first number is in fact wrong and so he tries a different number.

What is the probability that this is correct?

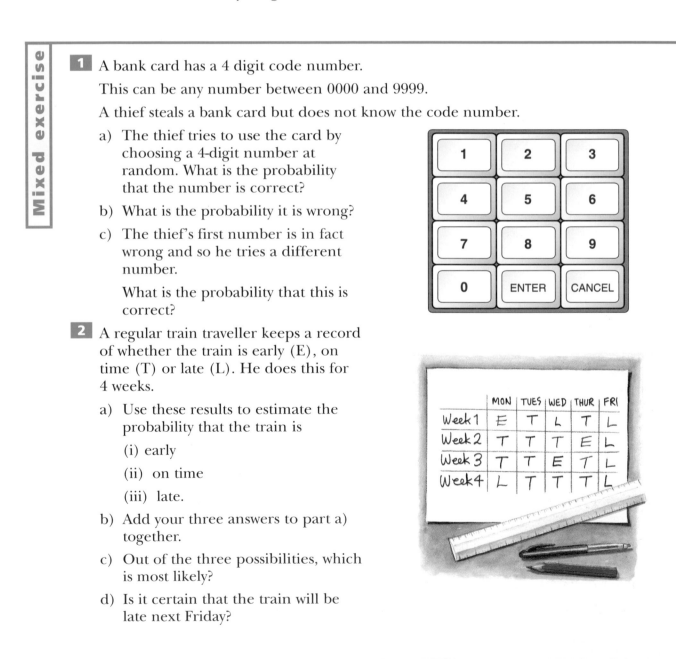

2 A regular train traveller keeps a record of whether the train is early (E), on time (T) or late (L). He does this for 4 weeks.

a) Use these results to estimate the probability that the train is

(i) early

(ii) on time

(iii) late.

b) Add your three answers to part a) together.

c) Out of the three possibilities, which is most likely?

d) Is it certain that the train will be late next Friday?

	MON	TUES	WED	THUR	FRI
Week 1	E	T	L	T	L
Week 2	T	T	T	E	L
Week 3	T	T	E	T	L
Week 4	L	T	T	T	L

Mixed exercise

3 Three people are taking the theory section of their driving test. There are 35 multiple choice questions each with four possible answers A, B, C, and D.

a) Richard guesses 32 questions and leaves 3 unanswered.

   How many marks does he expect to get?

b) Claire knows the right answers to 27 questions and guesses the others.

   How many marks does she expect to get?

c) Kunal thinks he knows the answers to 31 of the questions. He is right on all of these except 5 where he is wrong. He guesses the remaining questions.

   How many marks do you expect him to get?

4 This list gives all the possible outcomes when 3 coins are tossed.

Coin 1	Coin 2	Coin 3
H	H	H
H	H	T
H	T	H
H	T	T
T	H	H
T	H	T
T	T	H
T	T	T

a) Use the list to write down the probability of

   (i) 3 heads

   (ii) 3 tails

   (iii) 2 heads and 1 tail

   (iv) 1 head and 2 tails.

b) Show your four answers to part a) add up to 1.

c) What is the probability that all 3 coins come up the same?

d) What is the probability that all 3 coins do not come up the same?

5 In a game called Anagram, the letters of a word are written on cards. The cards are picked at random and put into a line. You have to find the word.

a) One time the cards show

   L I R G .

   What is the word?

b) Another time the word is POSSESSES. State the probability that the first letter picked is
   (i) S   (ii) P   (iii) E   (iv) O

Ask as many people as you can to choose a number between 1 and 10. Record their answers.

Are people more likely to choose some numbers than others?

Seventeen

Symmetry

★ This chapter looks at ideas you first met in Book 1.

★ Use this chapter to make sure you really understand them.

Reflection symmetry

The McDonald's logo has **reflection symmetry**. If you put a mirror on the dotted line shown, the logo looks exactly the same in the mirror as it does without the mirror.

The logo has **one line of reflection symmetry**.

The Royal Bank of Scotland logo has four lines of reflection symmetry.

These are shown with dotted lines.

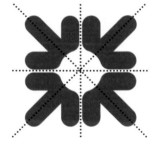

Rotational symmetry

The British Rail logo has no lines of reflection symmetry. However, it has another kind of symmetry, called **rotational symmetry**. When it is rotated through half a turn it looks exactly the same. So it has two positions in which it looks the same.

It has **rotational symmetry of order 2**

The NatWest logo has rotational symmetry of order 3.

 The Royal Bank of Scotland logo has rotational symmetry as well as reflection symmetry. What is its order of rotational symmetry?

1 Copy these shapes and draw in all the lines of reflection symmetry, if any. Write underneath the order of rotational symmetry, if any.

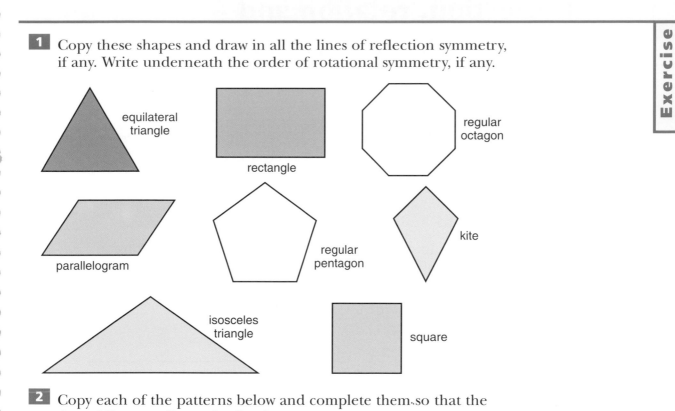

equilateral triangle

rectangle

regular octagon

parallelogram

regular pentagon

kite

isosceles triangle

square

2 Copy each of the patterns below and complete them so that the dotted lines are lines of reflection symmetry.

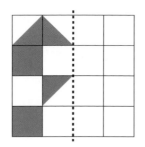 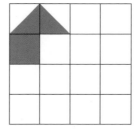

3 Copy each of the diagrams below and complete them so that they have rotational symmetry of the order stated.

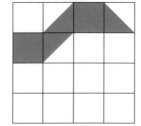 

Rotational symmetry of order 2   Rotational symmetry of order 4

Find some common signs and symbols (such as road signs) and describe their symmetries.

Reflection, rotation and translation

Fatima is designing a wallpaper. She draws her design on a grid of squares.

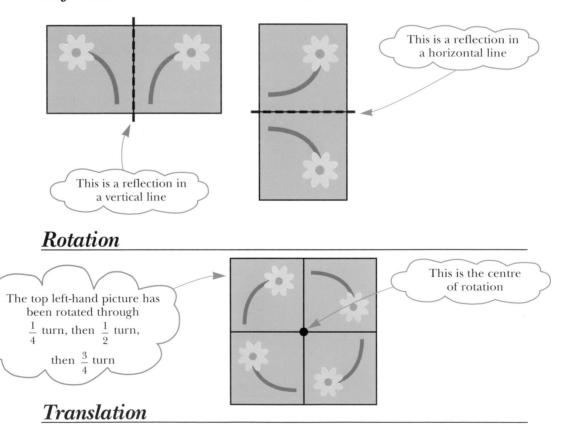

Fatima's design only has one picture in it. She has drawn the picture of a flower in different positions to make the wallpaper design.

There are three different ways that Fatima can change the position of the flower – **reflection**, **rotation** and **translation**.

Reflection

This is a reflection in a vertical line

This is a reflection in a horizontal line

Rotation

The top left-hand picture has been rotated through $\frac{1}{4}$ turn, then $\frac{1}{2}$ turn, then $\frac{3}{4}$ turn

This is the centre of rotation

Translation

In some cases the picture of a flower has been moved to a different position but is still the same way up.

Look at the flower in the top left-hand corner of the pattern at the top of the page. Count four squares to the right and two squares down and you will find another flower the same way up.

1 Make 6 copies of this diagram and use them to answer parts a) to f).

a) Draw a reflection of the triangle in the *y* axis.

b) Draw a reflection of the triangle in the *x* axis.

c) Draw a rotation of the triangle through $\frac{1}{4}$ turn clockwise about the origin.

d) Draw a rotation of the triangle through $\frac{1}{2}$ turn about the origin.

e) Draw a translation of the triangle 4 squares to the right and 2 squares down.

f) Draw a translation of the triangle 1 square to the left and 5 squares down.

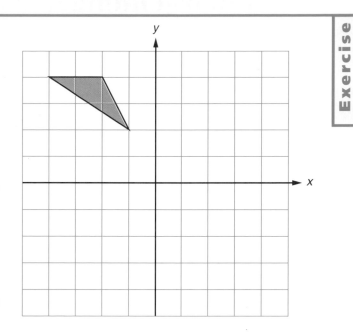

2 For each pair of shapes, write down what has been done to the first shape to get the second. Choose from:

- reflection in the *x* axis
- reflection in the *y* axis
- rotation of $\frac{1}{4}$ turn clockwise about (0,0)
- rotation of $\frac{1}{2}$ turn about (0,0)
- rotation of $\frac{3}{4}$ turn clockwise about (0,0)

a) A to F

b) C to G

c) D to C

d) B to H

e) F to E

f) C to E

g) H to C

h) A to E

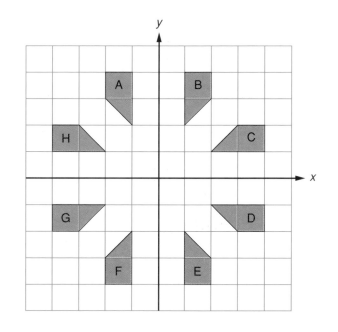

Design your own wallpaper or wrapping paper, using reflection, rotation and translation.

Look at real designs for some ideas.

Enlargement

Jason and Sharon are buying a new fitted kitchen. Jason makes a scale drawing of the kitchen on squared paper so that they can plan the kitchen.

This is Jason's drawing.

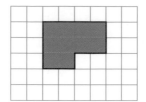

Sharon thinks that Jason's drawing is too small. She makes an enlargement of the drawing.

This is Sharon's drawing.

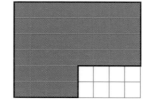

All Sharon's lines are twice as long as Jason's lines.

Sharon's drawing is an enlargement of Jason's with **scale factor 2**

Using a centre of enlargement

Another way to draw an enlargement is to use a **centre of enlargement**. The diagrams below show how to make an enlargement with scale factor 2 using a centre of enlargement C.

1. Draw lines from the centre of enlargement C to each corner of the shape.

2. Make each line twice as long.

3. Join up the ends of the lines to make the enlargement.

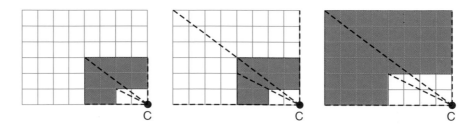

1 Which of these triangles are enlargements of triangle A?

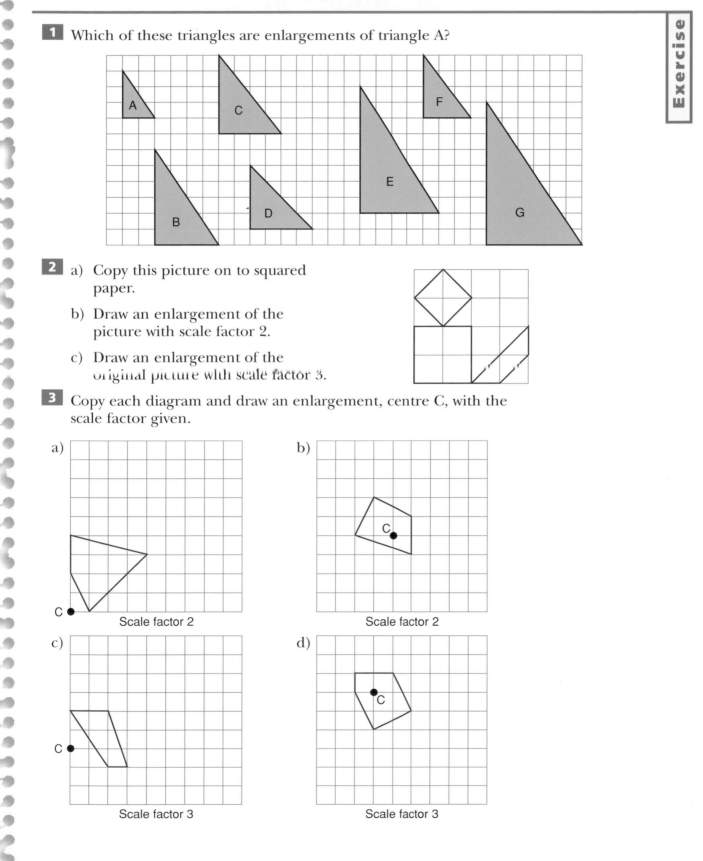

2 a) Copy this picture on to squared paper.

b) Draw an enlargement of the picture with scale factor 2.

c) Draw an enlargement of the original picture with scale factor 3.

3 Copy each diagram and draw an enlargement, centre C, with the scale factor given.

a)

Scale factor 2

b)

Scale factor 2

c)

Scale factor 3

d)

Scale factor 3

Finishing off

Now that you have finished this chapter you should be able to

★ find out how many lines of reflection symmetry a shape or pattern has

★ find out whether a shape or pattern has rotational symmetry, and if it has, give the order of rotational symmetry

★ draw the reflection of a shape in the *x* axis or the *y* axis

★ rotate a shape about its centre or the origin through $\frac{1}{4}$ turn or $\frac{1}{2}$ turn or $\frac{3}{4}$ turn

★ carry out and describe a translation of a shape

★ recognise and draw an enlargement of a simple shape using a whole number scale factor

★ recognise and draw an enlargement of a simple shape using a whole number scale factor and a centre of enlargement.

Use the questions in the next exercise to check that you understand everything.

Mixed exercise

1 For each of these patterns, say

   (i) how many lines of reflection symmetry, if any, it has

   (ii) whether it has rotational symmetry, and if it has, what the order of rotational symmetry is.

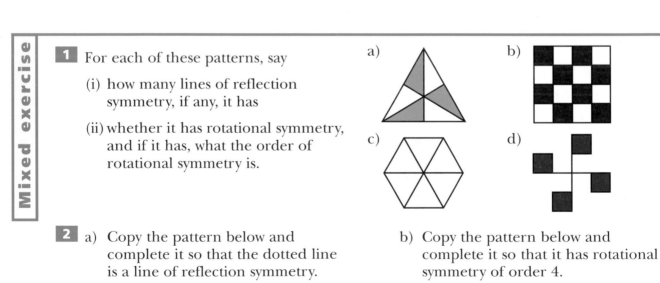

2 a) Copy the pattern below and complete it so that the dotted line is a line of reflection symmetry.

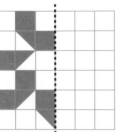

   b) Copy the pattern below and complete it so that it has rotational symmetry of order 4.

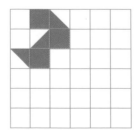

3 Copy this diagram.

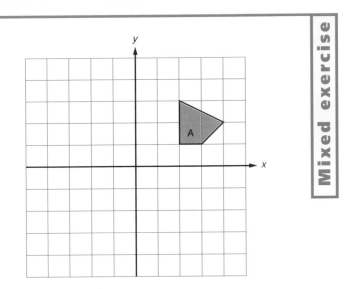

a) Reflect shape A in the *x* axis. Label this shape B.

b) Rotate shape B through $\frac{1}{4}$ turn clockwise about the origin. Label this shape C.

c) Translate shape C 2 squares to the left and 7 squares up. Label this shape D.

d) Reflect shape D in the *y* axis. Label this shape E.

e) Rotate shape E through $\frac{1}{2}$ turn about the origin. Label this shape F.

4 Marie has a photograph 10 cm by 6 cm. She wants to have it enlarged to fit one of the frames below. For each frame, say whether it is possible to enlarge the photograph to fit the frame, and if it is, give the scale factor of the enlargement.

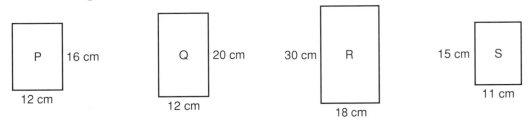

5 a) Copy shape A in question 3 on to squared paper.

b) Draw an enlargement of shape A with scale factor 2.

c) Draw an enlargement of shape A with scale factor 3.

d) Draw an enlargement of shape A with scale factor 4.

6 Make two copies of the diagram below and draw enlargements with scale factors 2 and 3, using centre of enlargement C.

Solid objects may have planes of symmetry instead of lines of symmetry. Where is the plane of symmetry of a person?
Describe the symmetries of a cube, a cuboid and a sphere.

Answers

Chapter 1: Using numbers

Page 5: Length, mass and capacity

1. a) 300   b) 600
2. a) 40   b) 25
3. 11
4. 1.2
5. a) 44 miles b) 86 miles
6. a) 24 km   b) 112 km
7. a) 3 kg   b) 2.5 kg
8. a) 2000   b) 8
9. a) Emily by 10 ml
   b) Ask your teacher to check your answer.

Page 7: Time

1. a) 0830   b) 1830   c) 1120
2. a) 9.45 a.m.   b) 10.30 p.m.
   c) 12.15 p.m.
3. a) 1527   b) 1402
4. a) Derek   b) Darren   c) 3 minutes 28 seconds
5. a) (i) 20 minutes   (ii) 35 minutes
      (iii) 30 minutes   b) 2010

Page 9: Directed numbers

1. a) £40   b) £45   c) –£20
2. –2 °C
3. a) 0.6 °C fall   b) 0.4 °C fall
   c) 0.1 °C rise
4. £60; £93; £21; –£107 (or £107 DR); –£92
   (or £92 DR); £458
5. a) £13 000 profit   b) £5000 loss
   c) £11 000 loss
6. a) –3   b) 2   c) 3
   d) –8   e) 9   f) 0

Page 11: Number patterns

1. a) 1, 2, 3, 4, 6, 12   b) 1, 2, 4, 8, 16
   c) 1, 3, 5, 15   d) 1, 2, 4, 7, 14, 28
   e) 1, 5, 25   f) 1, 2, 3, 5, 6, 10, 15, 30
   g) 1, 2, 3, 4, 6, 8, 12, 16, 24, 48
   h) 1, 2, 3, 4, 5, 6, 10, 12, 15, 20, 30, 60
2. a) 49   b) 8   c) 400   d) 125
   e) 10   f) 900   g) 27   h) 12
3. 7, 11, 13, 17, 19
4. a) 12   b) 18   c) 30
5. a) These are 1×20, 20×1, 10×2, 4×5, 5×4.
   b) 1, 2, 4, 5, 10, 20
6. a) 36   b) 100

Page 13: Index notation

1. a) 64   b) 32   c) 81   d) 64
   e) 216   f) 1296   g) 2.25   h) 15.625
2. a) 500   b) 70 000   c) 8000   d) 200 000
   e) 650   f) 5800   g) 2 400 000 h) 87 500
3. a) 7×10^3 b) 3×10^2 c) 9×10^4 d) 6×10^3
   e) 8.6×10^3 f) 5.7×10^4 g) 7.5×10^2 h) 2.9×10^5
4. a) 10^2 b) 10^3 c) 10^6
5. See question 1.

Page 15: Calculators

1. a) 7 000 000 000   b) 80 000 000 000
   c) 250 000 000 000   d) 3 200 000 000 000
2. a) 600 000 000 000   b) 4 000 000 000 000
   c) 8 000 000 000 000   d) 30 000 000 000
   e) 15 000 000 000   f) 2 200 000 000 000

Page 17: Brackets

1. a) 19   b) 27   c) 36
   d) 3   e) 8   f) 11
2. a) 17   b) 23   c) 10   d) 10
3. a) 15   b) 10   c) 22   d) 3
4. a) $4 + 5 - 3 = 6$ b) $(7 + 5) \div 3 = 4$
   c) $(2 \times 6) + 3 = 15$ d) $(5 + 2) \times 2 = 14$
   e) $3 \times (5 - 1) = 12$ f) $(3 \times 2) + 2 = 8$
   g) $(1 \times 6) - 2 = 4$ h) $(6 \times 6) \div 4 = 9$
   i) $8 + 2 - 3 = 7$ j) $(10 + 8) \div 2 = 9$

Chapter 2: Measuring and drawing

Pages 20–21: Reminder

1. 300 m
2. north-east
3. 750 m
4. a) 100°   b) 230°   c) 20°   d) 200°
5. a) 1 km   b) 240 m   c) 15 cm
6. a) 3.35 m by 2.20 m   b) 90 cm
   c) 195 cm by 105 cm   d) 1.8 cm

Page 23: Accurate drawings

2. b) 9.4 cm

Page 25: More shapes

1. e) 5.0 cm and 6.9 cm
2. b) 7.3 or 7.4 cm;   146 or 148 m

Page 27: Using bearings

1 a) A 030°, B 135°, C 315°, D 260°
   b) A 15 km, B 20 km, C 30 km, D 25 km
2 a) 225°   b) 45°   c) 280°
   d) 100°   e) 20°   f) 200°
   g) There is a difference of 180° between each
      pair of bearings.
3 1.8 or 1.9 km and 5.0 or 5.1 km

Chapter 3: Fractions

Page 31: Equivalent fractions

1 a) $\frac{14}{16}\left(=\frac{7}{8}\right)$ b) $\frac{4}{8}\left(=\frac{1}{2}\right)$ c) $\frac{3}{5}$ d) $\frac{5}{16}$

2 a) 4   b) 6   c) 6   d) 3
   e) 3   f) 10   g) 75   h) 30

3 a) 1   b) 1   c) 3

4 a) $\frac{7}{8}$ b) $\frac{1}{2}$ c) $\frac{5}{8}$ d) $\frac{13}{16}$

   e) $\frac{1}{2}$ f) $\frac{7}{10}$ g) $\frac{3}{2}\left(=1\frac{1}{2}\right)$ h) $\frac{7}{8}$

5 a) $\frac{5}{8}$ b) $\frac{3}{4}$ c) $\frac{7}{8}$ d) $\frac{1}{2}$

6 a) $\frac{3}{8}$ b) $\frac{5}{8}$

Page 33: Improper fractions and mixed numbers

1 a) $1\frac{3}{8}$ b) $2\frac{1}{3}$ c) $5\frac{1}{2}$ d) 5

2 a) $\frac{13}{4}$ b) $\frac{19}{8}$ c) $\frac{23}{16}$ d) $\frac{23}{4}$

3 a) $3\frac{1}{2}$ b) $5\frac{1}{8}$ c) $1\frac{5}{16}$ d) $3\frac{5}{8}$

   e) $1\frac{5}{8}$ f) $6\frac{1}{4}$ g) $1\frac{3}{8}$ h) $8\frac{3}{16}$

4 a) 3 miles   b) $3\frac{3}{4}$ miles

   c) $3\frac{1}{4}$ miles   d) 7 miles

5 4 litres
6 a) $1\frac{3}{4}$ hours   b) 11

Page 35: Fraction of a quantity

1 a) 50   b) 25   c) 50
   d) 15   e) 60   f) 56
2 £15
3 a) £6   b) £14
4 a) 8   b) 6   c) 18
5 a) 40 minutes   b) 60 minutes
6 £1.44
7 a) 54   b) 20

Chapter 4: Angles and shapes

Page 39: Angles round a point and on a line

1 $a = 120°$ $b = 80°$ $c = 160°$ $d = 80°$
   $e = 160°$ $f = 140°$ $g = 75°$ $h = 60°$
   $i = 72°$
2 C, H and I
   A, E and J
   B, D, F and G

Page 41: Parallel lines

1 a) *a, d, e*   b) *b, c, f*
2 $a = 76°$ $b = 104°$ $c = 76°$ $d = 108°$
   $e = 72°$ $f = 108°$ $g = 108°$ $h = 72°$
   $i = 56°$ $j = 56°$ $k = 76°$
3 a) $a = 69°$ $b = 62°$ $c = 49°$
   b) 180°

Page 43: Triangles and quadrilaterals

1 $a = 55°$ $b = 85°$ $c = 80°$ $d = 135°$
   $e = 37°$ $f = 117°$ $g = 65°$
2 $a = 105°$ $b = 42°$ $c = 33°$ $d = 42°$
   $e = 43°$ $f = 69°$ $g = 27°$ $h = 66°$
   $i = 66°$ $j = 59°$ $k = 59°$ $l = 55°$
   $m = 54°$ $n = 72°$ $p = 54°$ $q = 89°$
   $r = 89°$ $s = 37°$

Page 45: Interior angles of polygons

1 b) 720°, 1080°, 1440°, 1800°
2 a) 120°   b) 135°   c) 144°   d) 150°
3 a) 72°   b) 54°   c) 108°
4 a) 60°   b) 60°   c) 120°

Page 47: Exterior angles of polygons

1 hexagon 60°, octagon 45°, decagon 36°,
   dodecagon 30°.
2 a) They all add up to 180°.
   b) The interior and exterior angles make up a
      straight line, so they must add up to 180°.
3 a) 9 sides — 40°, 25 sides — 14.4°, 100 sides — 3.6°
   b) 9 sides — 140°, 25 sides — 165.6°,
      100 sides — 176.4°

Page 49: Tessellations

1 Ask your teacher to check your patterns.
2 These pentominoes tessellate.

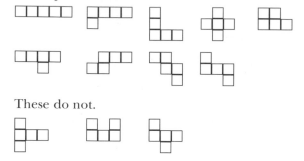

These do not.

Chapter 5: Decimals

Page 53: Tenths and hundredths

1 a) 7.4 m b) 14.68 m
2 Barcelona 1.7 m, Munich 1.2 m, Dublin 1.0 m, Vienna 1.5 m
3 a) $2\frac{3}{10}$ b) $4\frac{91}{100}$ c) $3\frac{7}{100}$ d) $5\frac{237}{1000}$
4 a) 3.9 b) 2.19 c) 5.03 d) 0.109

5
```
  |   +   + X |  +  X  +  | X |  +   |
  8       b)    a)     c)       9
```

6 £2.39
7 a) 1.08 m b) 1.78 m

Page 55: Multiplication and division

1 a) 17 b) 170 c) 1700
  d) 0.32 e) 0.032 f) 0.0032
2 a) 3 b) 0.8 c) 16.2 d) 3.12
3 a) 5 b) 8 c) 6.5 d) 20
4 a) £32.50 b) £325
5 £18
6 a) 86 °F b) 68 °F
7 £4.74
8 £12
9 a) 1.50 m b) 165 cm

Page 57: Fractions to decimals

1 a) 0.6 b) 0.375 c) 0.45 d) 1.25
  e) 0.32 f) 0.0625 g) 3.5 h) 2.6
2 a) $1.\overset{\cdot}{3}$ b) $0.\overset{\cdot}{1}$ c) 1.16 d) $0.\overset{\cdot}{4}$

Chapter 6: Sequences

Page 61: Patterns

1 a) 8, 10, 12 b) 20, 25, 30 c) 7, 9, 11
2 a)

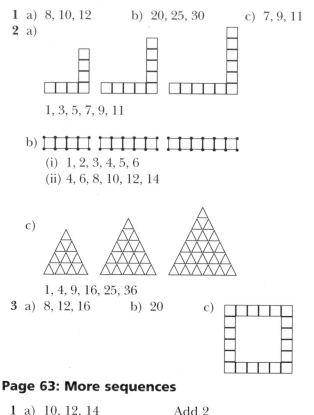

1, 3, 5, 7, 9, 11

b)
(i) 1, 2, 3, 4, 5, 6
(ii) 4, 6, 8, 10, 12, 14

c)

1, 4, 9, 16, 25, 36

3 a) 8, 12, 16 b) 20 c)

Page 63: More sequences

1 a) 10, 12, 14   Add 2
  b) 17, 21, 25   Add 4
  c) 6, 5, 4   Subtract 1
  d) 96, 88, 80   Subtract 8
  e) 2.5, 3, 3.5   Add 0.5
  f) 1, −1, −3   Subtract 2
2 a) 60 b) 15 c) 105
3 a) EVENS 26–32, EVENS 34–40, EVENS 42–48
  b) ODDS 49–63, ODDS 65–79, ODDS 81–95
  c) ODDS 65–79
4 4 September, 18 September, 2 October, 16 October
5 2000, 2004, 2008

Page 65: Finding *n*

1 a) Add 5 b) 21
2 a) Subtract 5 b) 8
3 a) £60, £70, £80,… b) £100
  c) Ask your teacher to check your arrow diagram.
  d) Amount saved = £50 + £10 × weeks after birthday.
    $A = 50 + 10 \times N$
  e) 8 weeks

Page 67: More number sequences

1. a) 8, 16, 32   Multiply by 2
   b) 40, 80, 160   Multiply by 2
   c) 27, 81, 243   Multiply by 3
   d) 10 000, 100 000, 1 000 000   Multiply by 10
2. a) 100, 50, 25   Divide by 2
   b) 100, 10, 1   Divide by 10
   c) 8, 4, 2   Divide by 2
3. a) 4 mm
   b) 1, 2, 4, 8, 16, 32
   c) $1, \frac{1}{2}, \frac{1}{4}, \frac{1}{8}, \frac{1}{16}, \frac{1}{32}$
   d) $\frac{1}{8}$ m^2

4. a) 2
   b) 4
   c) 5 years

Chapter 7: Percentages

Page 71: Percentages, decimals and fractions

1. a) (i) B   (ii) A   (iii) C
   b) 10% approximately
2. a) 12.5%   b) 50%   c) 37.5%
3. a) 20%   44%   36%
   b) $\frac{1}{5}$ $\frac{11}{25}$ $\frac{9}{25}$
   c) 0.2   0.44   0.36

Page 73: Percentage calculations

1. a) 200   b) 240   c) 150
   d) 66.5   e) 55.2   f) 1125
   g) 128   h) 227.5
2. a) £24   b) £50   c) £288
3. a) £8400   b) £4.50
4. £225
5. a) £1050   b) £1520

Page 75: Fractions to percentages

1. a) 20%   b) 35%   c) 36%   d) 37.5%
   e) 78%   f) 82.5%   g) 34%   h) 62.5%
2. a) 30%   b) 40%   c) 20%
3. a) Karen 50%,   b) Marie $33\frac{1}{3}$%
   c) Jo 22.9% approximately

4. a) £120 000   b) $28\frac{1}{3}$%   c) $31\frac{2}{3}$%

Page 77: Proportions

1. a) 0.75   75%   b) 0.25   25%
   c) 0.34   34%   d) 0.6   60%
   e) 0.8$\dot{6}$ 86.$\dot{6}$%   f) 0.24   24%
   g) 0.95   95%   h) 0.$\dot{7}$ 77.7%
2. a) 41   b) 0.585... or about 59%
   c) tennis   d) badminton
3. a) about 58%   b) about 32%
   c) about 57%
   d) Ask you teacher to check your answer.

Chapter 8: Co-ordinates and graphs

Page 81: Finding a point

1. a) 96   b) Letter is A or F   c) 1C, 4A, 8D, 14E, 16B
2. A(4, 8), B(7, 7), C(0, 5), D(6, 3), E(2, 2), F(7, 0)
3. The letter K

Page 83: Positive and negative co-ordinates

1. A(2, 2), B(0, 5), C(−2, 2), D(−1, 0), E(−2, −2),
   F(0, −5), G(2, −2), H(1, 0)
2. The letter M
3. a), b) Ask your teacher to check your drawing.
   c) When you add up co-ordinate values (without
   the 'sign') you get the number of blocks.

Page 85: Equations and graphs

1. a) (0, 1), (1, 2), (2, 3), (3, 4), (4, 5), (5, 6), (6, 7),
   (7, 8), (8, 9), (9, 10)

   b)

x	0	1	2	3	4	5	6	7	8	9
y	1	2	3	4	5	6	7	8	9	10

   c) The y co-ordinate is the same as the x
   co-ordinate add 1. $y = x + 1$
2. a) (i) (0, 3), (1, 4), (2, 5), (3, 6), (4, 7), (5, 8),
   (6, 9), (7, 10)

   (ii)

x	0	1	2	3	4	5	6	7
y	3	4	5	6	7	8	9	10

   (iii) The y co-ordinate is the same as the x
   co-ordinate add 3. $y = x + 3$
   b) (i) (0, 6), (1, 5), (2, 4), (3, 3), (4, 2), (5, 1), (6, 0)

   (ii)

x	0	1	2	3	4	5	6
y	6	5	4	3	2	1	0

   (iii) The x co-ordinate add the y co-ordinate is 6.
   $x + y = 6$

3 a)

x	0	1	2	3	4	5	6	7	8
y	2	3	4	5	6	7	8	9	10

  b) Ask your teacher to check your grid.

Page 87: More graphs

1 a)

x	0	1	2	3	4	5	6	7	8	9	10
y	400	350	300	250	200	150	100	50	0	–50	–100

  b) Ask your teacher to check your graph.
  c) He has no money left in the bank.
  d) After 9 months he is £50 overdrawn.
     After 10 months he is £100 overdrawn.

2 Ask your teacher to check your graph.

3 a) (i)

x	–3	–2	–1	0	1	2	3
y	0	1	2	3	4	5	6

   (ii)

x	–3	–2	–1	0	1	2	3
y	5	4	3	2	1	0	–1

  b) Ask your teacher to check your graph.
    The lines cross at $(-\frac{1}{2}, 2\frac{1}{2})$

Chapter 9: Statistics

Pages 90–91: Revision exercise

1 a) ◣ ; ◕   b) 20; 6; 10   c) 36

  d) Ask your teacher to check your bar chart.
2 a) Ask your teacher to check your frequency table.
  b) 20
  c) 30
3 Ask your teacher to check your charts and table.
4 a) 0   b) 1.5   c) 1.5   d) 5
5 a) 5   b) 26° C   c) 15 °C
6 a) 20   b) 1   c) 15   d) 40
  e) 2

Page 93: Pie charts

1 a) 90°, 120°, 150°
  b) Children £150 000   Adult £90 000
    Teenage £120 000
  c) $33\frac{1}{3}$ %

2 a) Ask your teacher to check your pie chart.
  b) 50%
3 a) 15   b) 15   c) 6
  d) Every time one team wins, another team loses.
4 a) 15°
  b) Ask your teacher to check your pie chart.
  c) 50

Page 95: Mean, mode, median and range

1 a) Mode 14, median 10, mean 11, range 6
  b) Mode 4, median 4, mean 4, range 6
  c) Mode 2, median 2, mean 2, range 4
  d) Mode 23, median 23, mean 23, range 4
  e) Mode 0, median 3.5, mean 2.6, range 6
2 a) 30
  b) (i) 4   (ii) 3   (iii) 3   (iv) 6
3 a) Ask your teacher to check your frequency tables.
  b) Mount Pleasant Street 1.8, Mandela Avenue 3
  c) Mount Pleasant Street 6, Mandela Avenue 6
  d) Ask your teacher to check your answer.

Page 97: Grouping data

1 a)

Number of plants growing	0–3	4–7	8–11	12–15
Description	Very low	Low	Medium	High
Frequency	7	2	3	8

  b) Ask your teacher to check your bar chart.
  c) Ask your teacher to check your answer.
2 a) Add up the lengths of the calls. The mean is
    $\frac{420}{20}$ = 21 minutes.
  b) $\frac{420}{7}$ = 60 minutes (or 1 hour)

  c) Ask your teacher to check your frequency chart
    and frequency polygon.
  d) 5 m to 9 m 59 s
3 a) Ask your teacher to check your tally chart.
  b) Ask your teacher to check your frequency table.
  c) Ask your teacher to check your frequency chart
    and frequency polygon.
  d) £2000–£2999 and £4000–£4999

Answers

Page 99: Scatter diagrams

1 a) no correlation
   b) positive correlation
   c) negative correlation
   d) negative correlation
   e) positive correlation
   f) no correlation
2 a) Ask your teacher to check your scatter diagram.
   b) Positive correlation. The more pages they type, the more mistakes they make.
   c) Mandy

Chapter 10: Formulae

Page 103: Finding a formulae

1 a) £40   b) £56
2 a) (i) £15 (ii) £50
   b) 20 weeks
3 a) 40 miles b) $C = 60 \times L$
4 a) £12.50   b) £8   c) £20

Page 105: Using formulae

1 a) $p = 2(l + w)$ b) $t = 3(a + b)$
2 a) 12 cm   b) (i) $p = 4a$
3 a) 14 cm   b) (i)(i) $p = 2x + 2y$
4 a) $2a + 2b$ b) $2a + b$
   c) $6a$
5 a) 48 cm   b) 48 cm, cube

Page 107: More formulae

1 a) 14   b) 12   c) 30
2 a) 16   b) 3
3 a) 14   b) 12   c) 30
4 a) $6(x + 2)$ b) 72^2
5 a) (i) a^3 cm^2 (ii) $6a^2$ cm^2
   b) volume = 8 cm^3 surface area = 24 cm^2
6 a) $ab + 2a^2$ b) 14
7 a) $3h$ b) 12

Chapter 11: Money

Page 111: Pay

1 a) £350   b) £180   c) £200   d) £225
2 a) £227.50 b) £237.50 c) £320
3 a) 29   b) £198
4 a) £10 800 b) £9000   c) £13 200
5 a) £1500   b) £75
6 April £1000; May £1018; June £994; July £952

Page 113: Tax

1 a) £6000   b) £8000   c) £15 000
2 a) £3200   b) £3750   c) £2640
3 a) £13 000 b) £2600   c) £13 400
4 a) Telesales £11 500; Marketing £13 000
   b) £1500
5 Yes (net salary is £18 750)

Page 115: Value for money?

1 Sofa   a) £720   b) £125
  Dishwasher   a) £1170   b) £175
2 Iron   a) £5.25   b) £35.25
  Calculator   a) £3.50   b) £23.50
  Ghettoblaster a) £26.25 b) £176.25
3 a) TV World by £5 b) They are the same price.

Page 117: Profit and loss

1 a) £15   b) £70   c) £30
2 a) £10 profit   b) £10 loss   c) £3 profit
3 a) £15   b) 60%
4 a) £4   b) $66\frac{2}{3}$%
5 a) £104   b) £24   c) 30%
6 a) £6.25   b) £31.25
7 a) £600   b) 20%

Chapter 12: Equations

Page 121: Unknowns

1 a) 4   b) 3   c) 10
2 A = 40 g   B = 20 g   C = 20 g
  D = 20 g   E = 15 g   F = 15 g
3 a) (i) 4   (ii) 6   (iii) 14
   b) (i) $x + 8 = 12$ (ii) $7 + x = 13$
   (iii) $x - 9 = 5$

Page 123: Solving equations

1 a) 2   b) 3   c) 1
2 a) $x = 2$ b) $x = 3$ c) $x = 10$ d) $x = 1$
3 a) $x = 3$ b) $x = 8$ c) $x = 6$ d) $x = 13$

Page 125: More equations

1 a) $x = 3$ b) $x = 3$ c) $x = 10$ d) $x = 2$
2 a) $x = 4$ b) $x = 5$ c) $x = 3$ d) $x = 2$
3 a) $x = 4$ b) $x = 5$ c) $x = 2$ d) $x = 2$
   e) $x = 3$ f) $x = 6$ g) $x = 7$ h) $x = 2\frac{1}{2}$
4 4 cm
5 a) $4a = 20$ b) 5 cm

Answers

Page 127: Trial and improvement

1 a) He should try a bigger number.
 b) $t = 8$
2 a) She should try a bigger number.
 b) $l = 5$
3 a) 9 years b) 19 years
4 45 and 50

Chapter 13: Ratio and proportion

Page 131: Proportion

1 a) 2   b) 10
2 a) 200 g   b) 75 g
3 a) £60   b) $\frac{1}{3}$
4 a) 4:3   b) 15   c) 75
 d) Ask your teacher to check your answer.

Page 133: Simplifying ratios

1 a) 2:1 b) 1:5 c) 4:1 d) 2:3
 e) 3:1 f) 3:1 g) 2:5 h) 5:8
2 a) 1:3 b) 200:1 c) 4:1 d) 2:5
 e) 1:6 f) 4:3 g) 2:5 h) 8:3
3 copper 300 g, zinc 150 g
4 Milton £36, Spencer £24
5 Ceri £7500, Andrea £12 500
6 a) (i) 2:3 (ii) 4:1 (iii) 2:1
 b) 5:3 c) $\frac{3}{8}$

Page 135: Best buy

1 4 litre box
2 6 pack
3 9 pack
4 750 g box
5 the garden centre
6 2.5-litre tin
7 they are the same.
8 a) (i) 64 (ii) £51.20 b) (i) 36 (ii) £53.64
 c) the smaller tiles

Page 137: Changing money

1 a) 9   b) 90   c) 540
2 a) 220   b) 1100   c) 5500
3 a) 2.28   b) 22.80   c) 34.20
4 a) £20   b) £2.27
5

1F	2F	3F	4F	5F
£0.11	£0.22	£0.33	£0.44	£0.56

10F	20F	50F	75F	100F
£1.11	£2.22	£5.56	£8.33	£11.11

6 Keyring (40 F) and vase (45 F)

Chapter 14: Area and volume

Pages 140–141: Reminder

1 a) perimeter = 36 cm, area = 55 cm^2
 b) perimeter = 42 cm, area = 78 cm^2
 c) perimeter = 36 cm, area = 50 cm^2
 d) perimeter = 32 cm, area = 24 cm^2
2 a) 10 m^3 b) 8 m^3 c) 24 m^3 d) 16 m^3
3 Ask your teacher to check your answer.

Page 143: Triangles

1 a) 4 cm^2 b) 7.5 cm^2 c) 5 cm^2 d) 8.75 cm^2
2 a) 15 cm^2 b) 14 cm^2 c) 6 cm^2 d) 7.5 cm^2
3 19.2 m

Page 145: Shapes made of rectangles and triangles

1 a) 1700 m^2 b) 1375 m^2 c) 2725 m^2
2 a) 10.5 cm^2 b) 13 cm^2 c) 10.25 cm^2

Page 147: Circumference

1 a) 25.1 cm b) 37.7 cm c) 31.4 cm
 d) 42.1 cm e) 60.9 cm
2 a) 6.4 cm b) 13.4 cm c) 5.4 cm
3 a) 219.9 cm   b) 455 times

Page 149: Area of a circle

1 a) 201.1 cm^2 b) 452.4 cm^2
 c) 78.5 cm^2 d) 63.6 cm^2 e) 43.0 cm^2
2 a) 2.52 cm   b) 3.48 cm   c) 1.87 cm
3 7.57 m^2
4 18.8 m^2
5 a) 12   b) 38.5 cm^2 c) 162 cm^2
6 1.78 m

Page 151: Cuboids

1 a) 504 cm^3 b) 270 cm^3 c) 180 cm^3 d) 240 cm^3
2 72 000 cm^3 (or 72 litres)
3 12.5 cm
4 162 cm^3
5 50 m

Answers

Chapter 15: Approximations

Page 155: Decimal places

1 a) 1.6   b) 3.8   c) 6.2
   d) 2.7   e) 55.2   f) 14.7
2 a) 3.58   b) 17.61   c) 2.81
   d) 10.48   e) 6.33   f) 0.40
3 a) one   b) two
4 a) (i) 7.7   (ii) 7.73   b) (i) 2.9   (ii) 2.88
   c) (i) 5.2   (ii) 5.17
5 a) £38.33   b) £38
6 55.1%
7 5.29

Page 157: Estimating costs

1 a) £48   b) £27   c) £23
   d) £38   e) £56   f) £57
2 rent £3000; gas £320; electricity £240; water £200

Page 159: Rough calculations

1 a) Mick 50 miles   Rajit 40 miles
     Julie 100 miles   Kath 110 miles
   b) No
2 600
3 a) 19   b) 11   c) 200
4 a) 1800 m^2 b) 10   c) 180 m^2

Page 161: Rough checks for your calculator

1 a) 101   b) 22 113   c) 1006
2 £1 + £1 + £1 + £2 + £2 + £1 + £3 = £11
3 a) £4   b) £2   c) £14
4 a) 12   b) 2   c) 12   d) 100
   e) 25   f) 30
5 a) 6000   b) 1500

Chapter 16: Probability

Pages 164–165: Revision exercise

1 a) (i) $\frac{1}{2}$ (ii) $\frac{4}{6} = \frac{2}{3}$ (iii) $\frac{1}{7}$
    (iv) $\frac{13}{52} = \frac{1}{4}$ (v) 0
   b) Ask your teacher to check your drawing.

2 a) (i) $\frac{35}{50} = \frac{7}{10}$ (ii) $\frac{15}{50} = \frac{3}{10}$ (b) 1200

3 a) $\frac{5}{250} = \frac{1}{50}$ b) $\frac{245}{250} = \frac{49}{50}$ c) $\frac{5}{249}$

4 a) (i) $\frac{3}{51} = \frac{1}{17}$ (ii) $\frac{16}{51}$ (iii) $\frac{32}{51}$
   b) They add up to 1 ($= \frac{51}{51}$)

5 a) (i) $\frac{3}{8}$ (ii) $\frac{5}{8}$
   b) Yes

Page 167: Two events

1 a)

		50p coin	
		Head	**Tail**
10p coin	**Head**	HH	HT
	Tail	TH	TT

   b) (i) $\frac{1}{4}$ (ii) $\frac{2}{4} = \frac{1}{2}$ (iii) $\frac{1}{4}$
   d) No
   e) HH, HT, TH, TT

2 a)

		Amelia		
		Paper	**Stone**	**Scissors**
Zoe	**Paper**	Draw	Z	A
	Stone	A	Draw	Z
	Scissors	Z	A	Draw

   b) (i) $\frac{3}{9} = \frac{1}{3}$ (ii) $\frac{3}{9} = \frac{1}{3}$
    (iii) $\frac{3}{9} = \frac{1}{3}$
   c) 1

3 a) Ask your teacher to check your table.
   b) 1 $\frac{1}{36}$,   2 $\frac{3}{36}$,   3 $\frac{5}{36}$,   4 $\frac{7}{36}$,   5 $\frac{9}{36}$,   6 $\frac{11}{36}$

Chapter 17: Symmetry

Page 171: Reflection symmetry

1 Equilateral triangle — 3 lines of reflection symmetry
rotational symmetry order 3
Rectangle — 2 lines of reflection symmetry
rotational symmetry order 2
Regular octagon — 8 lines of reflection symmetry
rotational symmetry order 8
Parallelogram — 0 lines of reflection symmetry
rotational symmetry order 2
Regular pentagon — 5 lines of reflection symmetry
rotational symmetry order 5
Kite — 1 line of reflection symmetry
no rotational symmetry
Isosceles triangle — 1 line of reflection symmetry
no rotational symmetry
Square — 4 lines of reflection symmetry
rotational symmetry order 4
2 Ask your teacher to check your patterns.
3 Ask your teacher to check your patterns.

Page 173: Reflection, rotation and translation

1 Ask your teacher to check your drawings.
2 a) reflection in the x axis
b) rotation of $\frac{1}{2}$ turn about (0,0)
c) reflection in the x axis
d) rotation of $\frac{3}{4}$ turn clockwise about (0,0)
e) reflection in the y axis
f) rotation of $\frac{1}{4}$ turn clockwise about (0,0)
g) reflection in the y axis
h) rotation of $\frac{1}{2}$ turn about (0,0)

Page 175: Enlargement

1 B, G
2 Ask your teacher to check your enlargements.
3 Ask your teacher to check your enlargements.

Index